Frequently
Asked
Questions
about the
Universe

Also by Jorge Cham and Daniel Whiteson

We Have No Idea:
A Guide to the Unknown Universe

Frequently Asked Questions about the Universe

Jorge Cham and
Daniel Whiteson

JOHN MURRAY

First published in the United States of America in 2021 by Riverhead Books
First published in Great Britain in 2021 by John Murray (Publishers)
An Hachette UK company

1

Copyright © Jorge Cham and Daniel Whiteson 2021

Book design by Alexis Farabaugh

A CIP catalogue record for this title is available from the British Library

Hardback ISBN 978-1-529-33104-2
Trade Paperback ISBN 978-1-529-33105-9
eBook ISBN 978-1-529-33107-3

Printed and bound in Great Britain by Clays Ltd, Elcograf S.p.A.

John Murray policy is to use papers that are natural, renewable
and recyclable products and made from wood grown in sustainable forests.
The logging and manufacturing processes are expected to conform to
the environmental regulations of the country of origin.

John Murray (Publishers)
Carmelite House
50 Victoria Embankment
London EC4Y 0DZ

www.johnmurraypress.co.uk

For Oliver

J.C.

♦

*For Silas and Hazel, whose constant stream of questions
inspired and interrupted the writing of this book*

D.W.

can get up to 3000°F. This is why our space shuttles and landing modules heat up on reentry from orbit, and it's why we put advanced ceramics and cooling systems in front of them to deflect and absorb the heat created by this air drag.

Rocks from space don't usually come with fancy shields to keep them cool, so they just get hot. *Very* hot. Depending on how hot they get, they might shatter in the atmosphere, exploding into smaller fragments that rain debris on the surface, or they might hang together and deliver most of their energy directly to the surface of Earth.

Small rocks (up to about one meter wide) actually hit Earth all the time but burn up in the atmosphere as shooting stars. If you catch them on a clear night, they are even beautiful to watch.

But as the rocks get bigger, they start to get more dangerous, and not even our atmosphere can stop them. To get a sense of scale, the table on the next page compares the amount of energy that asteroids of different sizes would have with the explosive power of the bomb dropped on Hiroshima in World War II.

Rocks that are five meters wide have about the same energy as the bomb dropped on Hiroshima. This sounds bad, but actually, scientists aren't too worried about them. These rocks often strike somewhere in the ocean or explode in the very upper atmosphere, usually far from populated areas.

Size of Asteroid	Explosive Power
5m	1 Hiroshima Bomb
20m	30 Hiroshima Bombs
100m	3,000 Hiroshima Bombs
1 km	3,000,000 Hiroshimas
5 km	100,000,000 Hiroshimas

Stepping up to twenty meters in size (about five elephants wide) means a rock carrying the same energy as *thirty* Hiroshima bombs. That's a huge explosion. If we get really unlucky and a rock that size makes it through the atmosphere and hits somewhere like Manhattan, it would be an enormous disaster. Millions of lives would be lost. But it wouldn't necessarily mean the end of the human race. In fact, a twenty-meter asteroid exploded in our atmosphere very recently.

In 2013 over Chelyabinsk, Russia, a twenty-meter-wide rock from the asteroid belt hit our atmosphere at sixty thousand kilometers per hour. It was midmorning, but the light from the explosion was reportedly brighter than the Sun and could be seen up to one hundred kilometers away. Around a thousand people were injured. It was spectacular enough to cause panic and widespread religious reawakenings, but not spectacular enough to end humanity's time on Earth.

Above that size (in the kilometer range) is where the danger zone for our species really begins. Scientists believe that the last arrival of a multiple-kilometer-size rock was sixty-five million years ago, and that it might have been what caused the extinction of the dinosaurs.*

You might be asking yourself: If Earth is thousands of kilometers wide (12,742 kilometers, to be precise), how can a relatively small rock of a few kilometers cause so much destruction? Let's consider the case of a humble, five-kilometer rock.

A five-kilometer-wide rock falling to Earth would carry something on the order of 10^{23} joules of energy. For comparison, the average American uses about 3×10^{11} joules of energy in a year, and all of humanity uses about 4×10^{20} joules. So this one collision would carry a thousand years' worth of human energy, all concentrated and delivered rapidly in a single spot. In nuclear-weapon units, that's two billion kilotons, or about one hundred million times the energy in the Hiroshima bomb.

That much energy released on land would create an explosive shock wave that would travel rapidly from the impact site, carrying with it enough heat and wind to destroy anything within thousands of miles. It would also cause earthquakes that shatter all the

---

* Interestingly, scientists think the rock that killed the dinosaurs (about ten kilometers wide) flew by Earth years before it actually hit our planet, which should have given the dino-scientists some warning.

land around it, and trigger enough volcanoes to soak the entire area in hot lava.

If you are anywhere near that impact, your fate is simple: you are toast. Charred, blackened toast that can't be improved no matter how much you butter it. How close do you have to be? In this scenario, Los Angeles is probably not far enough away from an impact that happens in New York.

But even if you are far from the impact area (say, on the other side of the world), you probably won't survive for very long. You might avoid the immediate blast, but you would still suffer the earthquakes and reignited volcanoes that the impact causes. Your larger problem, though, will be the cloud of superheated dust, ash, and rock fragments that will be thrown up into the atmosphere. Some of this superhot dust will drift away, roasting Earth's surface and torching forests. And it will hang out in the skies for a long, *long* time. This cloud would shroud Earth in darkness for years, or decades, or longer, which is probably what killed the dinosaurs.

You might wonder what would happen if the asteroid hits water rather than land. Unfortunately, things don't get much better. First, a lot of the initial energy would be absorbed by the water, creating a mega-tsunami with waves *several kilometers* high. Imagine yourself looking up at a wave that's four or five times bigger than the

Empire State Building. A wave that big means that *Denver* would suddenly become beachfront property, and Australia and Japan would get completely wiped off the map.

And that's just the immediate aftermath. A giant cloud of dust would probably kill most of our ecosystem, making life as we know it pretty unsustainable. And if the asteroid hits water, the impact would also put enough water vapor in the atmosphere to cause an accelerated greenhouse effect. This greenhouse effect would trap energy on Earth and heat the planet up to unlivable temperatures.

That's just what a five-kilometer rock would do. Now imagine what an even *bigger* asteroid would do!

How Likely Is It?

To get a sense of how likely it is for a large asteroid to hit us, and whether we would see it coming, we spoke to the good people working for NASA's Center for Near-Earth Object Studies (CNEOS), headquartered at the Jet Propulsion Laboratory in Pasadena, California. Really, their name should be "Asteroid Defense Force" because they are the group tasked with preventing the complete annihilation of the human race by a giant rock crashing into us. (And you thought *your* job was important.)

The main approach of CNEOS (together with their international collaborators) is to look for and keep track of all the rocks in the solar system, so that we might have a heads-up if any of them are on a path to hit us. Using telescopes, and after decades of hard work, the CNEOS team has created a pretty good database of all the biggest rocks around us, where they are, and where they will be in the near and far future.

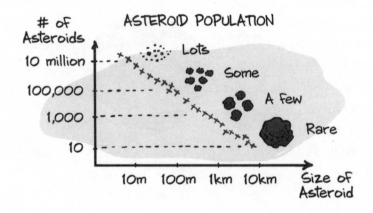

What they've found is that there is an inverse correlation between the size of the rock and how many of them there are in the solar system. Small rocks are plentiful in our neighborhood, but the really large rocks are hard to find. In other words, the bigger the rock, the rarer it is. This is good news because the rarer a type of rock is, the less likely it is to crash into us.

For example, CNEOS estimates there are hundreds of millions of rocks out there that are around one meter in size. That's a lot of rocks, and in fact, rocks of this size hit Earth all the time, about five hundred times per year. That means that on any given day, there is probably one of these rocks crashing somewhere on Earth. Fortunately, they cause very little damage.

OW, OW, OW...

As the rocks get bigger, they get rarer. For example, rocks that are five meters wide are in the tens of millions in the solar system, and strike Earth only about once every five years. Twenty-meter-size rocks (like the one that exploded over Chelyabinsk, Russia) are in the single millions, and on average only hit Earth every fifty years or so.

But what about the really large ones? Even if those are rarer (there are only a thousand rocks that are one kilometer wide, and just a few dozen greater than ten kilometers), you only need *one* of them to hit us to potentially end the human race.

Oof!

Oof!

Luckily, large rocks like that are not only rare but also relatively visible. If a large rock is on a regular orbit, it's likely that we'll have seen it reflect light from the Sun. That means the CNEOS team is fairly confident they know where most of them are. They've counted them and mapped their trajectories, and so far, none of them seem to be on a collision course with us.

At least, we don't think so. The good news is that we know where 90 percent of the big rocks in the solar system are. The bad news is that we don't know where 10 percent of the big rocks in the solar system are.

There could still be large rocks out there that we haven't seen. They might be hidden, or they could be on an orbit that hasn't brought them close enough for us to observe them. Remember that asteroids don't glow on their own, and a few kilometers in size isn't that big compared to the size of our solar system. That means there's still the possibility that a large asteroid can sneak up on us out of the darkness of space.

Deadly Snowballs

Much more concerning to the scientists at CNEOS are the other type of space rock that can hit us: giant snowballs (aka comets). While NASA has a good handle on most of the asteroids in the solar system that can kill us, it turns out that comets are much harder to spot.

Most comets we see are huge balls of rock and ice that fall in from the Oort cloud toward the Sun on very long orbits. Sometimes these orbits can take hundreds or thousands of years to go around the Sun. That means that when a comet visits the inner solar system (our cosmic neighborhood), it might be the first time that we see it.

Even worse, after their long trip from the cold cosmic suburbs, they are going to be moving much more quickly than an asteroid, which means (a) we won't have time to react (a year at best), and (b) they would have a more devastating impact if they hit us.

Scientists think that the chance of a comet crashing into us is probably rare, but it's hard to estimate. Very recently, it happened to one of our neighbors: in 1994, the comet Shoemaker-Levy 9 broke into twenty-one pieces on its way toward the sun, and those fragments crashed into Jupiter. One of those pieces created a gigantic explosion approximately the size of Earth.

In fact, it was this comet collision that sparked NASA to create the Near-Earth Object program to catalog and track all near-Earth objects. After all, if it happened once, it can happen again, and maybe to us.

What Can We Do About It?

Let's say a comet suddenly comes out of the blue and is on a path to hit us. Or let's say that we find a new big asteroid we haven't seen before and we learn that its orbit intersects with ours in the future. Or let's say that some kind of solar system event knocks a big rock straight toward us. Is there anything we could do about it?

In the movies, all it takes is a musical montage of scientists in lab coats, a pot of coffee, and a whiteboard full of scribbles to figure out a solution (plus, it helps if you have Bruce Willis). But is that realistic?

Surprisingly, this is something that groups like CNEOS actively think about, and according to them, the strategies for surviving a big rock coming our way fall into one of two categories.

Option #1: Deflect

The first option is to try to deflect the asteroid or comet—that is, to nudge its trajectory so it's not on a collision course with us. Scientists have a few good ideas for how to do this:

Rockets: This plan involves shooting a rocket at the incoming rock to either crash into it or blow up enough of it to change its trajectory. It might also be possible (though less likely) to land on the rock and use the booster engine to push the rock into a new trajectory.

Digger: Another idea is to send a giant crane or robot to land on the rock and start digging, pushing the debris out into space. The momentum from all the debris would essentially cause the rock to change course.

Lasers: Another fun idea would be to build a huge laser here on Earth and then shoot it at the asteroid or comet. The goal would be to heat up one side of the rock so that the melting ice or vaporized rock would push the rock out of Earth's path.

ASTEROID DEFLECTION TECHNIQUES

Mirrors: If you wanted to get really fancy, you could send a set of lenses and mirrors to gather sunlight and focus it onto the rock. This would boil off some of its material, pushing the rock out of its collision course.

Option #2: Destroy

The second option is, of course, to try to destroy the big rock before it gets to us. In other words, nuke it.

One idea is to launch a nuclear missile that intercepts the rock and blows it up, hopefully shattering it into smaller pieces that would then burn up in our atmosphere. Some of them may still hit the ground, but that's a better outcome than if the whole rock struck Earth.

On the other hand, it might be that the incoming asteroid is mostly just a pile of rubble loosely bound together by gravity. In that case, a single nuclear explosion wouldn't be very effective at dispersing the rock, and we would be better off sending a series of smaller nukes. Perhaps we would optimize the distance of the nuclear blasts for maximum dispersal, perhaps setting them off a bit above the surface so that they do more deflecting than destroying.

Of course, the most crucial factor that determines whether any of these strategies will work is how much time we have. According to

Good thing we have extra nukes.

CNEOS, "the three most important things you need in order to survive an asteroid or comet impact are: (1) early detection, and (2) the other two don't really matter much."*

If we have a lot of warning (years, hopefully), then we might have time to build and deploy one of these strategies. Not only that, but more time also gives us greater opportunity to affect the outcome.

For example, if we learned that a particular asteroid would strike Earth in one hundred years, any small nudge we give it today would have a huge impact in its future trajectory. It's like firing a sniper rifle at a target one kilometer away. The slightest deflection of the rifle to the side will give you a large sideways displacement of the bullet over the full kilometer it travels. The same is true for asteroids: if you see one coming far enough in advance, you only need to give it a little push to knock it off course.

This is why it's so important to keep track of all the asteroids and comets flying around us, and why the idea of one of them coming out of the blue is so scary.

* That's an actual quote from Dr. Steve Chesley, senior research scientist at CNEOS, who graciously agreed to be interviewed for this chapter.

Should You Worry?

Before you start building that underground bunker or go on a shopping spree for canned foods, we should probably tell you that the probability of an asteroid coming to kill us all is actually not that high.

In the short term, the team at NASA and the few dozen people working on this around the world are doing everything they can to spot these rocks early, and they are quietly doing a solid job so that you don't have to keep looking up with anxiety. They are confident that nearly all of the planet-killing rocks have been spotted and are accounted for and pose negligible risk to Earth. There are even plans for more powerful telescopes, like the Near-Earth Object Surveillance Mission space telescope and the Vera Rubin ground telescope, that will vastly increase humanity's ability to detect rocks earlier. Thinking about your personal risk, you are much more likely to get killed by something on Earth (a car crash, a fall in the shower, getting strangled by your pet gerbil) than a rock from space.

But it's always good to remember that the universe is unpredictable, and that there are limits to our science. Perhaps there is a large asteroid with our name on it lurking in our solar system, or maybe there is a comet coming from afar aimed straight at us. Predicting anything with certainty in a complex solar system like ours is a tough order. Do you remember that asteroid that exploded over Chelyabinsk, Russia? It came out of nowhere. The only warning we had was when it hit the atmosphere.

The truth is that we live in a chaotic cloud of rocks and planets, all of them pushing and pulling on one another in an intricate gravitational dance. Every collision or close approach should give us pause, and it should motivate us to support science further so we can understand more about our galactic neighborhood. It should also get us thinking about humanity's ability to work together, and whether we can set aside our differences for our own survival.

Because if we can't dance that dance, well . . . just remember what happened to the dinosaurs.

Are Humans Predictable?

Let's take a moment to think about the choices you make. For example, you chose to pick up this book, and you're choosing right now to read these words. There, you did it again. You made the choice to read *these* words, too. *And these.*

AND THESE.

Okay, by now you're probably tempted to *stop* reading these words, just to prove that you have a choice and that we are not in control of you. After all, you have free will, right? Go ahead and look away for a moment if it makes you feel better. We'll wait for you.

Are you back? Great choice. (We totally predicted that.)

The point is that we all like to think that we are in charge of our own actions. As we go about our day, we make hundreds, if not thousands, of decisions. Should I get out of bed or hit the snooze button? Should I shower today? Should I eat bacon and eggs for breakfast, or a warm bowl of oatmeal? The world is your oyster, and if you wanted to have oysters for breakfast, you could do that, too. We don't recommend it, but hey, it's your choice.

It's your choice.

This feeling of control makes us uncomfortable with the suggestion that any of our choices are predetermined, or that they can be predicted. We like to believe that when we decide to do something, it happens *at that moment*, not before, and that no one could have foreseen it.

But is that really true? Are our choices truly unpredictable? As science has advanced and our understanding of the laws of physics has grown more and more complete, a lot of people have begun to wonder if it's possible to predict what a person is going to decide. Or to take the question out of the lab and into the halls of philosophy: Do we really have a choice when making decisions? Or can the actions of a complex, thinking being be reduced to a simple set of predictable laws?

The answer, should you choose to read it, lies ahead. But be warned: we predict you probably won't like it.

Physics in Your Brain

As far as we know, everything in the universe follows the laws of physics. To date, we haven't found a single thing that doesn't follow them. The laws we've discovered and have improved over the centuries seem to be true for everything, from bacteria to butterflies to black holes.

And since *you* are also in the universe, the laws of physics apply to you, too, and to your brain, which is the center of your thinking being. Brains and black holes are made of the same stuff (matter and energy), so the same rules that apply to black holes also apply to brains.

How can physics help us understand the brain? Is there a law that predicts how many cookies you will eat today, or whether you'll choose a banana instead? Unfortunately, there's no outright Newton's second law of cookies, or Einstein's banana brain equation. Physics can describe something like the brain, instead, by breaking it down into smaller, simpler pieces that we can understand. Then we add all the pieces together to see how the whole thing works.

This is just like when you were a kid and you took a toaster apart to see how it worked. Hopefully, unlike your toaster, we'll be able to put your brain back together again.

Your brain can be broken down into lobes, and those lobes can be broken down into neurons. Each neuron is essentially a little electrical switch that gets "on" or "off" signals from other neurons. Then, based on those signals, the neuron might send an on or off signal out to other neurons.

Your entire brain is made up of these neurons. A tangle of eighty-six billion of them, all wired together by over one hundred trillion connections. Together, this huge network of simple biological switches makes up who you are: your memories, abilities, reflexes, and thoughts.

And that's pretty much it. That's all your brain is: a bunch of simple switches, and lots of connections.

Just like an electrical switch, each neuron's output is determined by the input it gets and the little biological circuit inside of it. Neurons don't have moods or whims. They don't fire because they "feel" like it. Each neuron simply follows the rules that are programmed into its genetic makeup.*

---

* It's a little more complicated than that, because neurons can change and adapt. But even then, each neuron is following rules for how to change and how to adapt, so the point is the same.

Does that mean that brains are predictable? After all, if a neuron is simply following rules, then you should be able to predict what a neuron will do. And if you can predict what a neuron will do, then you should be able to predict what a whole bunch of neurons connected together will do. And if you can do *that*, then you could in theory predict what a human will do.

Not so fast. There are certain things about the brain that make it not so easy to predict. Those things have to do with chaos theory and quantum physics.

A Chaotic Brain

While neurons don't have moods, they are still a sensitive bunch.

Even if something is purely mechanical, like a perfectly tuned machine or a rigid computer program, that doesn't mean it will always give you the same result. For example, you don't always get heads when you flip a coin. Even though a coin follows the laws of physics when you throw it up in the air and when it hits a surface, it's still very hard to get it to land on the same side every time. That's because a coin flip is very sensitive to small changes in how you throw it: a small flick of your fingers, an errant air current, or a tiny bump on the table where it lands can affect whether the coin settles on one side or the other.

In the same way, neurons are very sensitive to small changes in their inputs. Neurons work by adding up the on or off signals they get from other neurons, weighing them depending on the strength of each connection. If the sum of all the signals crosses over a threshold, then the neuron activates and sends an on signal downstream to all the neurons connected to its output. But if the sum doesn't meet the threshold, the neuron stays silent. You can imag-

THE NEURON GAME

Neuron receives signals from other neurons...

The total signal reaches a threshold...

The neuron sends a new signal to other neurons, etc.

ine that a single input signal (out of thousands), or one small change in the strength of one connection, can make the difference in whether a neuron gets activated.

This sensitivity gets even more dramatic when you connect a lot of neurons together. A small change in one neuron can lead to a cascade of consequences that give the network a whole different output. For example, that small change can mean the difference between whether you choose to eat the cookie or the banana.

When a system is that sensitive to small changes, physicists say that it's "chaotic." It's the same reason why physics can't predict the weather very well. We can predict what one raindrop does, but weather is made up of a lot of water drops and air molecules that are sensitive to being bumped by each other (and by the wind, the mountains, cold air pockets, etc.). These effects don't cancel each other out; they build on each other, becoming larger and larger. If you have zillions of drops, then getting the direction of one of them slightly wrong now might make your prediction about tomorrow's rainstorms totally wrong. Add pesky butterflies that keep flapping their wings and the whole thing becomes so chaotic that it's impossible to predict.

Like rainstorms, brains are chaotic. You might try to predict the behavior of one neuron and do a pretty good job. But what happens if your prediction isn't perfect? For example, maybe your model of one neuron is 99 percent accurate, which is pretty good. (A 99 percent on a math test is an A+.) But 99 percent right also means 1 percent wrong, and when you try to predict the next set of neurons, those errors are going to propagate and grow. Extrapolate that to eighty-six billion neurons and you can see why predicting what your brain is going to do is very, very hard.

Eventually, though, science might figure out how to predict even the weather. If you have enough computing power (and enough time), it is theoretically possible to simulate anything to a perfect degree. In fact, the majority of the world's supercomputers today are dedicated to building increasingly more precise models of Earth's weather. You might imagine a computer in the future so large and powerful that it can perfectly simulate every neuron and connection in your brain with accuracy down to the molecular level.

Does that mean that in the future, scientists might be able to create some new kind of supercomputer to model your brain and predict your snacking decisions? Not if your brain is also quantum mechanical.

Your Quantum Brain

If your brain is chaotic, does that mean that it's unpredictable? Not necessarily. Just because a system is chaotic doesn't mean that it's unpredictable. It can be hard to predict what it's going to do, but it's still predictable. After all, it's still following the laws of physics, and the laws of physics can be simulated and therefore predicted.

But what if the law of physics themselves can make something unpredictable?

When you peel back a few layers of reality and look at the particles that make up everything around us, you learn something strange about the universe: the rules that apply to perfect machines and computer programs don't also apply to quantum particles.

Ideally, giving a system the same input conditions will give you the same output, but this *is not true* for quantum particles like electrons. What does that mean? It means that if you poke a quantum particle exactly the same way more than once, it *doesn't* always respond the same way. One time it might bounce back; another time it might ignore you entirely.

QUANTUM FICKLENESS

How is that possible? Well, electrons still follow the laws of physics, but they do it in a particular way. The laws of quantum physics don't specify exactly what happens to an individual electron. Instead, they specify what is more or less *likely* to happen. What *actually* happens for a single individual electron is randomly drawn from that list of possibilities. In other words, the laws of physics at the quantum level don't tell you what *will* happen; they tell you what *can* happen, and with what odds.

Poke the same electron the same way several times, and you will get different outcomes each time.* If you poke it enough times, you'll start to see a pattern (e.g., that it bounces back 75 percent of the time, and ignores you the other 25 percent of the time). This pattern *is* predictable by the laws of physics. But on any particular

---

* Doing the same thing over and over again and expecting different results is sometimes used as a definition of insanity. But it's totally reasonable in the quantum realm!

poke, what the electron does is *not* determined by the laws of physics but by a completely random choice made by the universe (not by the electron).

If that seems bonkers, it's because it *is* bonkers. We're used to things having a clear cause and effect: if I push on a chair, the chair will move in that direction. But that only happens at the macroscopic level. At the microscopic level, things are truly random.

This is important to our question because neurons are made out of quantum particles. In fact, everything you know is made out of quantum particles, which are not predictable.

Wait, What?

At this point, you might be a little confused. We just told you that neurons are made out of quantum particles, and that quantum particles are random (and thus unpredictable). Does that mean that neurons are also unpredictable?

Again, not necessarily.

Looking around, we don't notice a lot of weird quantum effects. We don't see cookies randomly disappearing from the package, just popping out of existence or quantum tunneling into your stomach.

Cookies and other large things seem to follow predictable rules. So why are large things so different from small things?

There are two reasons for that difference: (a) the randomness of quantum particles is very, very small compared to your cookie, and (b) for most things in our world, that randomness averages out to nothing. Let's tackle these ideas one by one.

The Randomness of Quantum Particles Is Very Small

Quantum particles are extremely small compared to a cookie or a neuron. A single neuron is made of more than 10^{27} particles. So the quantum fluctuations of a single particle (whether it moves here or there) are so small that they aren't likely to make a big difference. For example, if a single cell in your body moved to the right a little bit, would you feel it? Probably not.

The Quantum Randomness Tends to Average Out

More likely than not, the quantum fluctuations of all the particles in a neuron will cancel out. If the neuron has a particle that does a weird quantum move to the right, that effect will most likely be corrected by another random particle that moves to the left. In other words, any little unpredictable quantum wiggle tends to get drowned out by the wiggles from all the other particles.

These two ideas are true of everything that is much bigger than quantum particles. In fact, that's why it took physicists a long time to discover quantum mechanics: because you only see it on really, really small things. If basketballs and raindrops were suddenly veering off course or acting randomly, we would have discovered quantum physics much earlier.

But remember, just because quantum effects are small and usually average out doesn't mean that they can be totally ignored. Are big things, like neurons, totally unaffected by quantum randomness? The truth is, we don't know! It's conceivable that neurons *are* sensitive to random quantum fluctuations in a significant way, and that these fluctuations affect whether a neuron gets activated. If that's the case, then there *would* be an element of randomness in our brain circuits, which means you could never truly predict what anyone is going to think or do.

Unfortunately, we don't have any evidence right now that neurons are sensitive to quantum randomness. Some famous physicists have supported this idea, but so far there haven't been any experiments that show that neurons exhibit true quantum randomness. Other physicists try to make connections between quantum randomness and philosophical concepts like consciousness and free will. But so far, these arguments are as persuasive as Nigerian email scams.

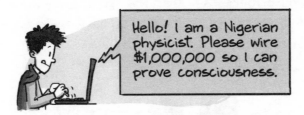

Did We Get It Right?

To summarize, your brain is both chaotic *and* quantum. But to what extent that means you are predictable is debatable.

If the brain is sensitive to quantum mechanical effects, then your decisions have a random element that is impossible to predict. Not just hard, *impossible.* As in, literally nobody knows what you are going to do next.

And even if your brain is not sensitive to quantum mechanical effects, chaos theory makes it almost impossible for anyone, or anything, to predict what you're going to think and do. While it might be possible in principle to perfectly simulate your eighty-six billion neurons and their one hundred trillion connections, it's almost certainly impossible in practice in the near future.

So it seems that, for now, you can rest assured that your brain (and therefore you) are not predictable. But is that the same thing as being in control of your decisions?

Being unpredictable is not quite the same thing as being *in charge.* Randomness is not the same thing as having control. If your brain is *random*, that doesn't mean that *you* are making any decisions; it means the universe is tossing dice and deciding what you do. Maybe your "you-ness" is the same as everyone else's you-ness: you (and we) are the universe.

If you rolled your eyes at that new age conclusion, then we can totally predict what you're going to do next: you're going to stop reading this chapter.

Where Did the
Universe Come From?

When you look up at the majesty of the night sky, or marvel at the intricate beauty of the microscopic world, you can't help but wonder: Where did it all come from? Why does the universe exist at all? What, or who, is responsible for this?

People have been marveling at the universe and guessing at its origins for a long time. Certainly, for far longer than we've had physics or cartoons. These questions are important because they might shed light on the context of our existence. We want to know *how* we came to be because it might tell us *why* we are here and how we should spend our time. If you knew where the universe came from, it might change how you live your life.

So what can physics actually tell us about this, the biggest of all questions?

In the Beginning

Before we ask where the universe came from or how it came into being, we need to back up a little. The first question we should ask is: Did the universe come into existence, or was it always here?

You might be surprised to learn that physics has a lot to say about this question. Unfortunately, a lot of what it has to say isn't very unified. In fact, our two great theories about the universe, quantum mechanics and relativity, point us in two very different directions on this topic.

The Quantum Universe

Quantum mechanics tells us that the universe follows unfamiliar rules. According to the theory, particles and energy behave in strange and uncertain ways. That can be pretty confusing, but fortunately, that's not the part of quantum mechanics that's relevant to the question at hand. That's because quantum mechanics is actually *crystal clear* about the past and the future of the universe.

Quantum mechanics describes things in terms of quantum states. Quantum states tell you the probability of what might happen when you interact with a quantum object. For example, it might tell you the probability of a particle's position. You might not know where a particle is right now, but you can know where it's *likely to be*. Quantum states are interesting because if you know what the state is for a quantum object today, you can use it to predict what the state is going to be tomorrow. Or in two weeks. Or in a billion years. The most famous equation in quantum mechanics, the Schrödinger equation, isn't about cats and boxes. It tells you how to take what you know about the universe and project it forward in time. And it also works backward: you can take what you know about the present and it will tell you what the universe was like in the past.

Schrödinger's
Sabertooth

According to the theory, there's no time limit to this predictive power. It's a bedrock principle that quantum information doesn't disappear; it just gets transformed into new quantum states. That means that if you know the quantum state of the universe today, you can calculate its quantum state at *any point in time*. Quantum mechanics tells us that the universe stretches backward and forward in time forever.

This means something very simple: the universe has always existed and will always exist. If our understanding of quantum mechanics is correct, there is no beginning of the universe.

The Relativistic Universe

Einstein's theory of relativity tells us a very different story. One problem with quantum mechanics is that it usually assumes that space is *static*, like a fixed backdrop where you can hang particles and fields. But relativity tells us that this is very wrong.

According to relativity, space is dynamic in the sense that it can bend and stretch and compress. We can see it bend around heavy objects like black holes or the Sun. And Einstein's theory also describes how all of space is expanding. Space isn't just a flat emptiness; it gets distorted locally by heavy things, and it is growing and getting bigger.

This is a crazy idea that first came from the mathematics of relativity, but we now have experimental proof of it. Using telescopes, we can see that galaxies are being pushed away from us faster and faster every year. Everything in the universe seems to be getting more spread out and colder, like a gas cooling as it expands.

What does this mean for the origin of the universe? Well, if you run the clock backward, our observations predict that the universe

(1) Quantum mechanics is mostly right.

(2) Relativity is mostly right.

(3) Neither of them is right.

Let's dig into these possibilities and see what they say about our universe's origin.

Quantum Mechanics Is Mostly Right

One possibility is that quantum mechanics is mostly right, and the universe has always existed and will always exist. Of course, the biggest problem with the quantum picture of the universe is that it doesn't describe how space is growing and changing, and it doesn't describe how the universe came from an extremely hot and dense state fourteen billion years ago.

What if we could keep most of quantum physics, and add a quantum explanation of how space can change? That might give us the answer we're looking for.

Quantum gets
spacey

To do this, some physicists have tried to paint a different picture of space. We're used to the idea of space as something fundamental: things exist inside of it, and it allows things to have a location and move around. As far as we know, it doesn't exist inside anything else.

But what if that's not true? What if there's something deeper and more fundamental than space? What if space is actually made up of smaller quantum bits, ones that can sometimes get organized together to have the familiar properties of space?

We see this kind of thing all the time in physics, and we call it "emergent phenomena." For example, liquid water, steam, and ice are all emergent phenomena of the same thing: water molecules and how they interact with one another depending on their temperature and pressure. In the same way, it might be that space itself emerges, and is stitched together from, more basic bits that are the essential units of the universe.

What are these quantum bits of the universe? Each theory is different, but here is what we can say about these bits:

(a) They each represent a location. At each location, you can have particles and fields, and therefore you and other things.

(b) They are not arranged in order. These bits are not sitting neatly in rows somewhere. Instead, they exist as a sort of quantum foam.

(c) They are related to each other by quantum relationships called "entanglement," where the probability of one can affect the probability of the other.

These theories say that what we call our universe is actually a network of these quantum bits connected to each other in a special way.

They also say that what we perceive as "space" is really just the strength of the connections between the bits in the network. For example, quantum bits that are strongly entangled are locations that we perceive to be close to each other. And bits that are weakly entangled are locations what we perceive to be far from each other. In this way, space emerges as the fabric that holds all of these bits together.

"Space"

QUANTUM BITS

This makes sense from a quantum point of view because it reflects what we see in our universe. Things that are close to each other (heavily entangled) are likely to affect each other, and things that are far away (less entangled) are less likely to affect each other. For example, if a star goes supernova on the other side of the universe, you can shrug it off and enjoy your lunch. But if a nearby star goes supernova, then your lunch is toast (as are you).

Hey, neighbor!

Whoa, where'd you go?

This also makes sense from a relativistic point of view because it allows space to be flexible. It could explain the bending of space as a temporary change in the relationships (or entanglements) between quantum bits that are near a heavy object. And it would explain how our universe can be expanding: new quantum bits are getting entangled with the current network, effectively making more space, which we see as the universe getting bigger.

This idea may sound crazy, but it gives us a clear answer to the question "Where did the universe come from?" According to this view, the universe came from a larger metauniverse filled with these quantum bits, and what we call "space" is really just a blob of those quantum bits that happen to be connected to one another.

This idea also has some interesting implications. If our universe exists as a blob of connected bits in a quantum metauniverse, then there could be other universes out there. Our blob universe could exist along with other blob universes, each with different ways in which the quantum bits are connected. It also means there might be a lot of space out there that is *not* connected to any particular universe. There might be quantum bits in this foam that are unconnected, or are connected together in incoherent ways. In other words, there might be a lot of non-universe in existence.

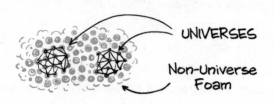

Of course, even if this idea answers the question of where *our* universe came from, it also raises more questions. Namely, what

All of this tells us that if relativity is correct, the universe didn't come from anything. It means that the universe came from itself, in a way. Both time and space started together, and it makes no sense to think about what came before. According to relativity, the universe is its own origin.

Neither of Them Is Right

The final possibility is that neither quantum mechanics nor relativity is right. Maybe the universe *didn't* always exist (as quantum mechanics requires) and it also never "started" (as relativity suggests).

Sometimes in physics, you get an answer that doesn't really make sense because you've asked the wrong question. For example, asking the question "Where did the universe come from?" assumes that the universe had to come from somewhere. It also assumes that there is an alternate possibility, as if there are conditions under which the universe could have *not* existed.

But what if the universe just is? What if it *had to be*, and the alternative, that the universe not exist, is not really a valid option?

This might sound like kooky philosophical semantics, but there is actually a very mathematical argument that supports it. In fact, it's the most mathematical argument possible: What if the universe itself is mathematical?

In physics, we use mathematics to describe the laws of the universe. It is the language of physics. But what if math is more than a useful way to count your stars or solve physics problems? What if math doesn't *describe* the universe but *is* itself the universe?

In this view, the universe is a mathematical expression, a raw concept of logic and possibility. It exists in the same way that the number 2 exists, or the equation "3 + 7 = 10" exists. Nobody ever asks, "Why does the number 2 exist?" or "Where does the number 2 come from?" It just . . . is. In the same way, some physicists and philosophers say that the universe exists *because* it works mathematically. All the laws of physics that describe our universe make sense, and therefore they are.

In fact, these physicists imagine that *all* sets of laws of physics that make sense mathematically *must be real and exist.* For example, there might be a set of laws of physics in which gravity is three times stronger, or one that has a fifth fundamental force of nature. If the equations work and the laws don't have any logical inconsistencies, then according to these physicists, that universe must exist. Just like all numbers or all logical equations (like "1 + 1 = 2") exist, so must any self-consistent universe formulation. And if a potential set of laws of physics doesn't work, then a universe with those laws must fizzle out or never come to be.

Can this be real? It might be. Many physicists are skeptical, because currently there seem to be a lot of different ways that one could build a set of mathematical rules for a universe. For example, string theory, a potential theory of quantum gravity, has 10^{500} variations, all of which are consistent with our universe.

But maybe it's just that our theories are unfinished. It may be that once we complete our understanding of the laws of nature, we will find a single valid theory that tells us there is only one possible mathematical universe. In that case, our universe wouldn't just *have* to be; it would also be the only way *to* be.

How Can Something Come from Nothing?

If you came to this chapter hoping we would answer this fundamental question about the universe, you are not alone. Unfortunately, most of these theories seem to tell us that the universe didn't come from anything. They tell us that maybe it always existed, or maybe it *had* to exist, or maybe it doesn't make sense to even ask where it came from.

It could be that this reflects physicists' preference for deflecting the question. After all, if you can show that the universe came from something, you then have to ask: Where did that something come from? The cycle would never end.

But deflecting the question is a little frustrating because it flies in the face of a very ingrained preconception we have about the universe: that everything has to come from something.

From early in our education, and from our everyday experience, we learn that nothing ever comes for free in this universe. We are taught to believe that energy is always conserved and that things don't mysteriously appear out of nothing. There is always a reason, and our human brains have evolved to look for those reasons.

But actually, we've learned in the last few years that even this basic idea isn't necessarily true. When we look out at the universe, we see that space is actively expanding, and new space is being created all the time. That new space isn't empty; it's filled with nonzero vacuum energy. With it, new particles can pop into existence, bringing new energy and matter into our universe.

This means two things. First, the universe is still being born (in other words, it hasn't finished "coming" from anywhere). Second, it is possible for energy to spontaneously appear. It's happening all around us as we speak.

So maybe the question "Where did the universe come from?" isn't the best question we could be asking. The universe exists, and maybe it exists for no other reason than for us to marvel at it and learn from it.

Maybe the real question we should be asking is, "What are we going to do with it?"

Will Time Ever Stop?

E ventually, everything in life seems to come to an end.

Lazy summer afternoons, secret boxes of cookies . . . even punishing winter storms and broken hearts don't last forever. Time ticks forward, and inevitably, both joy and pain fade into the past, making room for the present. The one thing that never seems to end is time itself.

It would be nice to know if time will end someday, or, at the very least, if time can be stopped. It would help you plan out your life, or maybe hit the pause button every once in a while to savor a particular happy or meaningful moment.

But can time be stopped? Will it end one day, or will it keep marching forever toward an infinite future? Will time one day . . . run out of time?

Can Time End?

Unfortunately, there's a lot we don't know about time. In physics, we know that it connects different configurations of the universe. For example, if you throw a ball straight up in the air here on Earth, we know that after some time it will be back where it started. That's what physics is all about: describing how the universe moves forward with the passage of time. The laws of physics tell us what is allowed to happen, and what is forbidden with respect to time.

But can it ever end or stop? The answer might depend on what we mean by time stopping. Let's examine some possibilities.

Does It Mean "No More Laws"?

Time is the thing that orders and connects all the different ways that the universe can be. So when time stops, maybe all the rules go out the window. Since the laws of physics are based on time and dictate what should happen as time ticks forward, perhaps an end of time simply means the death of *order*. Cause and effect might no longer have any meaning, and the universe would exist in a state of complete disarray. The death of order is not something we like to think about.

Does It Mean "No More Changes"?

Or perhaps an end of time simply means that the universe can't change anymore. If time is the thing that allows the universe to change, then when time stops, the universe might . . . *freeze*. Whatever state everything is in (balls flying through the air, lightning striking from a cloud, stars collapsing into black holes, etc.), that state would become fixed. And possibly forever: If time stops, can it just stop for a *little while* and then start up again? That would require some outside clock to be counting the number of frozen moments (more on that later). If time freezes, then maybe *all* clocks freeze, and the universe might never recover.

Does It Mean "The End"?

It's hard to imagine the universe existing without time. Relativity tells us that time is very closely related to space, and that they are better seen as the combined idea of "space-time." Perhaps that means that they are tightly connected, or even part of the same thing. It might even be that the universe existing *at all* is connected to the existence of time itself, and that without time there is no universe. This means that the only way for time to end is for the whole universe to end as well.

All of these possibilities point to a more fundamental question about time and the universe: Can the universe exist without time? In other words, can there *not* be time?

To answer that, let's recap what we know about time.

What We Know About Time

Time as a subject is actually not that well understood in physics. It's so ingrained in our theories about how the universe works that very few scientists have made any progress on the question of whether the universe can exist without it. Think about it: any experiment to test it basically requires time. You have to compare your experiment before and after a certain event, and without time the words "before" and "after" don't make sense. It even takes time to come up with the experiment!

But over time (no joke intended), physicists have gotten some important clues about the nature of time and how it relates to the universe. Specifically, we've learned the following:

(a) Time had a beginning (of sorts).

(b) Time is relative.

(c) You *could* have no time.

Let's dig into each of these clues one at a time.

Time Had a Beginning (of Sorts)

Until recently, most scientists believed that the universe was infinitely old and static. That means that the universe had always existed the way it is and, by extension, would always exist the same way. When we looked out into the night sky, not much seemed to move. The stars changed position a little with the seasons, but they didn't seem to change from year to year or even century to century. That the universe had always been that way, with stars hanging motionless in space, felt like a natural idea.

But when astronomers looked more closely, they made some shocking discoveries. Using techniques that let them measure the distance to faraway stars, they were amazed to discover that some of the smudges they thought were gas clouds were actually entire galaxies. And these galaxies seemed to be almost impossibly far away. Even more amazing, the light from these galaxies was shifting in color, which meant that the galaxies were moving away from us. It seemed that the universe was much larger than they had imagined, and it was hurrying to get bigger.

All of a sudden, we understood that the universe was not a static panorama of stars fixed in space; it was growing and changing. More discoveries revealed that it was getting cooler and less dense.

This gave humans a completely new view of the universe and its history. Because if the universe is expanding and cooling now, then what was it like in the past? If we run time backward, then we can imagine that the younger universe was denser and hotter. But we can't run time backward *forever*.

At some point, this backward picture of the universe gets so small and hot that it reaches a wall, a point of infinite density known as a "singularity." This singularity is what we project our universe's past to be, and it breaks down all of our theories about the universe. Even general relativity, which tells us how space curves around matter, can't describe the singularity, where the curvature becomes infinite. We don't know what happens to time and space under such extreme conditions. But it might represent a back end to our timeline of the universe.

In fact, some theories, which try to fuse general relativity with quantum mechanics, suggest that the singularity could be more than just a special moment in time. They suggest that space and time are so intertwined that you can think of this moment as the actual *start to time itself.* In other words, a beginning of time.

And if time had a beginning, could it also have an end?

Time Is Relative

We also know that time has a lot of strange properties, none more so than the fact that it doesn't flow at the same rate everywhere. In some places in the universe, time moves faster than in others. It's hard to believe, but physics tells us that there's no central cosmic clock keeping the universe in sync. Instead, every point in space has its own clock, and how quickly or slowly it ticks depends on how fast you are going and how close you are to a heavy mass such as a black hole. If someone is moving by you really fast, you will see their time moving slower than it does for you. And if they are near a black hole, and you are far away from it, you will also see their time moving slower than yours.

There's a common misconception that this means time slows down *for you,* as if you would feel time moving more slowly. But you don't. If you are zooming past someone, or are near a heavy object, other people will see your clock moving slowly, but you always feel time moving normally.

It's all about where you are and how fast you're moving relative to the clock. If you're on board the spaceship with a clock, you're not moving relative to the clock. And if you're near a black hole, then the clock is also there with you. In both cases, the clock will seem to run normally to you. But if you left someone back on Earth, then *they* see your clock run slowly because they are not with you.

Does this mean that time can stop or end? Not necessarily.

At half the speed of light, time on board a spaceship appears to go about 15 percent slower. At 90 percent of the speed of light, time on the ship is just over twice as slow, and at 99.5 percent of the speed of light, it is almost ten times slower than normal. If ten hours have passed on Earth, the spaceship clock would only appear to count a single hour. But while we can make the clock on the ship tick forward as slowly as we want by speeding up the ship, it will never actually stop. To stop time on the ship's clock, it would have to fly *at* the speed of light, which is not possible for anything with mass.*

In the same way, for someone watching you from afar, the clocks on your ship will appear to run slower as you get close to a black

---

* Which, of course, makes you wonder: How does a photon experience time? Flying through the universe at the speed of light, it sees everything else moving relative to it, and so all of the clocks in the universe look like they are frozen in time.

hole. As we talked about in What Happens If I Get Sucked into a Black Hole?, you'll start to look like you're moving in super-slow motion to someone far away. When you reach the edge of the black hole, you'll actually appear to be almost perfectly frozen in time, waiting for the black hole to grow and engulf you. But from your point of view, time will flow normally and the trip into the black hole will be seamless.

So you can't stop or end time by strapping yourself to a rocket and going really fast or going to a black hole. But if you need some extra time to work on your physics homework, just convince your teacher to jump on a spaceship so her clocks run slower than yours. Then you can take your time.

You *Could* Have No Time

Time is so basic to our experience that it's hard to conceive of a universe without it. But that doesn't actually mean that it's a core part of the universe. It just means that our thinking may be too narrow or subjective. The history of scientific discovery reminds us to check our preconceptions because our limited experience isn't always universal.

A fish that has lived in a flowing river its entire life can't imagine water without feeling its *flow*, but we know it's possible. The idea of water flow is not a deep and necessary component of the universe, but something that happens under certain circumstances. In other words, there can be water without flow.

Some physicists think that the same thing could be happening with time. It's possible that time is not a basic permanent fixture, but a special condition, just like the flow of the river. To make this theory work, you would need something else, call it "meta-time," from which regular time emerges. This meta-time can flow like time, or it can . . . just not. When this meta-time flows, we feel the effects of time. And when it doesn't flow, we feel that time ends.

It might be that some basic rules that we think are absolute and necessary, like causality and time only moving forward, are only special cases of this meta-time flow. Maybe this meta-time can do other things, like form the equivalent of whirlpools or waterfalls, and we would see time moving in loops. Or maybe it can break causality and you can eat dessert before dinner.

Of course, that doesn't mean there are *no* rules or that anything goes. This meta-time still has to have some similarity to our idea of time or it wouldn't be possible for time to flow at all. It still has to follow some rules, and if it does, then those rules might dictate a situation where time as we experience it can stop.

What this means is that time (as we know it) doesn't *have* to exist, and that there can be a universe without our familiar kind of time.

We don't have any evidence to suggest this is actually our reality.

But it's not *entirely* speculation. We know that our understanding of space and time breaks down fourteen billion years ago when the universe was very hot and dense, which leaves an opening for us to consider creative ideas.

How Would Time End?

At this point, we are well beyond the comfort zone of physics and into a region where we have to start guessing. But that's just how science works. New ideas about how the universe works aren't usually born as complete mathematical concepts all at once. Instead, they develop step-by-step, with the pieces coming together gradually over years, decades, or centuries. We sometimes explore wild paths until a coherent picture that can actually be tested by experiments takes shape. It's like building a house of cards, not from the bottom up but by holding each card in midair until you assemble the other cards around it.

What we know so far suggests there are several ways in which time can end.

The Big Crunch

One possible way for time to end is to mirror the conditions in which it began. We think that time might have started when the universe was hot and dense and space was unimaginably compressed in the Big Bang. What if the universe somehow returns to that state in a *reverse* Big Bang? Would time end then?

Big Bang   Big Awkward Teenage Years   Big Crunch

In fact, it might. We know that the universe expanded rapidly in its first moments, and has continued to get bigger in the billions of years since. That expansion has accelerated, so that galaxies are moving away from us faster every year. But we don't understand what's causing that acceleration. We call it "dark energy," but a cool-sounding name doesn't really tell us what's going on. And since we have no idea what is expanding the universe, we have almost no way to predict what it will do in the future. For example, that acceleration could stop and then reverse. Instead of increasing the speed at which other galaxies are flying away from us, it could slow them down, and eventually stop them and turn them around. Instead of stretching space into a bigger and bigger universe, this force may compress it, hurtling these spinning galaxies toward a massive cosmic collision known as the "Big Crunch."

What would happen if all of the matter and energy in the universe is compressed again into a tiny space? The truth is that nobody knows. It would be just like the conditions of the Big Bang, which are also a mystery to us. But that doesn't stop us from having fun thinking about it!

It could be that time will simply end along with the rest of the universe. It doesn't have to be an abrupt end. It could be a curved end in the same way that, for example, the direction of north ends at the North Pole. Time would just be capped at that point, and there would be no more time beyond that.

It could also be that space and time continue, even if all the matter and energy of the universe gets crunched into a singularity. Causality and the rules of our universe would continue to operate, but everything would be weird and unfamiliar, without the particles or the forces we are used to. In that case, time wouldn't end, even if the universe is unrecognizable.

Or it could be that the singularity creates another Big Bang and a whole different universe comes into being. This new universe could still be connected to our universe through a thread of time, which means that time doesn't end; it just starts again. If this is true, then that thread of time would connect an infinite number of universes both forward and backward in time.

The Heat Death

Another way in which time could end is through sheer boredom. To understand this, we need to think about why time marches forward in the first place. It seems like something is turning the crank on the universe's internal clocks, and is only turning it in one direction.

This is something physicists have puzzled over for a long time, even before there were physicists.* It strikes them as odd that time has two directions, but it only goes one way. There must be something, physicists argue, that makes time go forward instead of backward, like a deeper engine to which time is shackled.

THE GREAT HAMSTER OF TIME

And some physicists think they have found it. The universe does have a sort of built-in direction marker: entropy.

It's easy to misunderstand entropy, and to confuse it with general messiness or disorder. But that's not necessarily the case. We say that something has more entropy if there are more ways to arrange its internal particles. For example, if you require that a bunch of matter be clumped together in a corner, there are fewer ways to arrange it than if you let the particles spread out wherever they want. The same is true for temperature: there are fewer ways to arrange a blob of stuff if it has to have hot spots and cold spots than if it's all even temperatures, where any particle can be in any spot.

---

* Physicists don't like to think about this, the BP Era.

One funny thing about entropy is that it steadily marches upward as time goes forward. Our universe started with very low entropy, squeezed as it was into a very organized, dense state, and it's been expanding and gaining entropy ever since.

But the other fascinating thing about entropy is that it also has an edge: a state of *maximum possible entropy*. When everything has cooled and spread out completely evenly, entropy has hit the ceiling and can't go any higher. More importantly, it can't go any lower either. Once all the sand in the hourglass has fallen to the bottom, it can't flow back up again and the universe is stuck.

What does that mean for time? This state, known cozily as the "heat death of the universe," means that it's no longer possible for the universe to do anything useful. Most of the things you want to do (make a planet, charge your phone, run a lap) require energy to flow, which is only possible if there are places where it's imbalanced or concentrated (like your phone battery). But if all those imbalances have been smoothed out and everything has reached maximal entropy, then you can't do anything useful. Energy can't flow, like water in a perfectly level and still puddle. You made it to the end of the universe, but there's nowhere (or nothing) to charge your phone.

Some physicists look at the correlation between time and entropy and are tempted to say that time flows forward *because* entropy increases. The second law of thermodynamics says that entropy and time always increase together. These physicists suggest that if entropy reaches a maximum, then time itself will also stop!

Of course, this seems like a big leap, since (a) we don't know if entropy actually drives time forward, and (b) maximum entropy doesn't mean that the universe stops moving. Even at maximum entropy, particles can still fly around. The only limit is that they can't *increase* (or decrease) the overall entropy. It might be that the universe continues at this state of maximum entropy, but time keeps flowing.

It would certainly *feel* like the end of time, though. At maximum entropy, the universe will sit as a bland puddle, and nothing interesting can or will ever happen again. So while it may not be the end of time, it will definitely be the end of fun.

PARENTING AT THE END OF TIME

Who Knows?

If time is not a fundamental property of the universe, but just something that happens under some special conditions of a "meta-time" (like the flow of a river), then it's possible for those conditions to end.

Maybe we'll reach the end of our river in meta-time, causing time (as we know it) to unravel so it no longer ticks forward. The universe could then exist in a state without time, like a river without flow (or a lake). This new state would be wildly different than anything we have ever experienced or imagined. Without time and space, events in physics would not be causally connected. The universe would just exist as a frothing mass of unconnected quantum randomness.

To understand this requires us to know how quantum mechanics and space play together, a theory that physicists since Einstein have been fruitlessly searching for. This means we can't even fathom how it would work, or what might cause all those conditions to change. For all we know, it could happen tomorrow or the day after. Only someone with an outside view of the flow of this meta-time would know.

But this end of time could also be temporary. Like a lake that then feeds a different river, the meta-time could still evolve and pull the complex threads together to make time flow again.

Interestingly, we might not even notice if time stops and starts again. We measure time by physical processes that step forward regularly: a ticking clock, sand falling down an hourglass, electron atoms jumping between states, and so on. So if time unravels or stops, then those clocks would also stop. That also includes you, since you are a physical being. And since your thoughts and experiences can only happen if time moves forward, you wouldn't be able to tell when the flow of time stops or slows down. Like a character in a paused movie, you would have no idea how many times, or for how long, you were frozen.

The End of Our Time

It's time to admit the truth: we don't really understand time. Somehow, like the mysteries of our own minds, living in time doesn't necessarily give us insight into how it works.

We do have some beginnings of ideas. It might be that time is eternal, and the universe's clocks will tick forward forever into the infinite future. It might also be that time is not fundamental to the fabric of the universe but a special arrangement that might not last forever. Or it might be that time *is* fundamental to the universe, and the only way for time to end is for the universe to cease to exist.

Right now, time seems to be flowing smoothly. But who knows, maybe special circumstances like the Big Crunch or the heat death will reveal something new.

We might be wondering about this until the end of time.

Is an Afterlife Possible?

Sadly, everybody dies.

We're all stuck with that terminal condition called human life, which means our bodies won't last forever. Eventually, they will stop working, and our physical selves will give way to entropy and decay. But is the end of biological life also the end of *you*?

I guess a meteor's a pretty cool way to go.

This might be the deepest and most ancient of questions: What happens after we die? It's a question with so much emotional resonance that it's at the heart of most religions and cultures. The variety of ideas about the afterlife is truly impressive, and sometimes even a bit nutty. For example, we all go to a giant banquet hall in a huge space tree? C'mon, Norse mythology.

Usually, this is a topic that scientists leave to philosophers and religious scholars. But we have learned a lot about how the universe works since we started thinking about this question thousands of years ago. Is an afterlife possible given what we know about the laws of this universe?

The Physics of Heaven

There are lots of ideas about what life after death might be like. In most religions, this involves you existing in some new, non-earthly situation. What this new situation is like depends on the religion: sometimes it means existing among the clouds with angel wings and harp recitals (or the opposite: in a dark underworld with pitchforks and fire), and sometimes it means riding around with the Sun or singing endless songs over mugs of ale with warrior-gods. In most cases, this afterlife lasts forever, making everyone a little jittery about what kind of accommodations you'll have once you get there.

Also, in most cases, you're somehow still *you* in the afterlife. Your individuality, consciousness, and memories all somehow survive, making it possible for you to experience and be self-aware in this new phase of your eternal existence.

Is any of that possible, scientifically? Could you somehow be transmitted to another realm where you could continue to exist, as you, but now with a toga or extra-comfy slippers? Let's take it at face value and think about how that might work. Scientifically, these are the three key elements that seem to define a traditional afterlife:

(1) There's a *you* that can outlive your physical body.

(2) That *you* is captured and transported to another location.

(3) You exist in that other location, still able to experience things, forever.

Let's think about each of these elements one at a time, and see whether there's a version of these ideas that's compatible with what we know about the physical universe.

A *You* Beyond You

Most religions assume that there's a part of you that can survive the death of your body. The first step to understanding whether any of this makes sense scientifically is to figure out what part of you we are actually trying to preserve. For example, most of us are not interested in continuing to inhabit our own deceased bodies, staggering around like zombies and grossing out all of our former friends.

So if we are willing to let go of our physical bodies, then what is it that we want to preserve? What, exactly, makes you *you*?

This is the kind of question that science can really dig its teeth into. Physics operates in the realm of the physical (duh), and so it assumes that everything follows the laws of physics. And as far as we can tell, what makes you *you* is just . . . your particles. More specifically, the *arrangement* of your particles.

You see, it turns out that everything we see in our world is made out of the same building blocks. All the matter that we interact with is made out of two types of quarks (an "up" and a "down" quark) and electrons. And that's it. The two types of quarks can combine in different ways to make neutrons (one up quark + two down quarks) and protons (two up quarks + a down quark), which then combine with electrons in different proportions to make every element in the periodic table. And from those elements you get everything from llamas and boats to microbes.

In other words, there's no difference between you and every other thing (or person) in this world except for how those elements and particles are arranged together. A kilogram of you has pretty much the same particle content as a kilogram of lava, or ice cream, or elephant. If you were to write a cookbook for making anything on this planet, every recipe would have the same list of ingredients: a three-to-one ratio of quarks to electrons.

A PHYSICS COOKBOOK

But as anyone who has failed in the kitchen knows, a recipe is more than a list of ingredients. If you mix the raw materials the wrong way, you can get something that not even your dog will want to eat. In the case of you, the crucial thing that differentiates you from lava and ice cream and bugs is the *arrangement* of your particles, not the particles themselves.

In fact, there isn't even anything special about the exact particles that you're made out of. From the point of view of physics, all electrons are the same. If you swapped out your quarks or electrons for a fresh set and put them back exactly where your old ones were, nothing would change.

This means that you are just the *information* about how those particles are arranged, which means that you *can* survive even if your body dies. All you have to do is somehow copy that information and have it live on somewhere else.

Transporting You to Another Location

The next step in most afterlife scenarios is that you (whatever it is that makes you *you*) are somehow transported to another realm or location. From a physics point of view, this means that your information is somehow copied or transferred away from your body and taken to another place. But this raises several important questions:

✦ How is this information read or captured (or raptured)?

✦ Does all of your information get copied, or just part of it?

✦ Which version of you gets to go on?

The first question, "How is this information read or captured?" is really more of a process question. Whatever mechanism takes you to the afterlife must be based on some physical principle if it is to work within a logical universe. To date, we do have technology that can scan your body, like an MRI or a CT scan. And we have technology that can detect individual atoms. Both of these technologies are getting better every day, which means it's not inconceivable to think that someday soon there will be a process that can scan your body down to the atoms or particles.

But from a physics point of view, there are two problems you run into. First, any scanning would require imparting energy on your body. To detect individual particles, you would need to see them somehow, and typically that means hitting it with a photon or some other particle. On top of that, the universe doesn't allow you to copy quantum information without a cost. This is a core principle of quantum mechanics called the "no-cloning theorem," which says that quantum information can't be copied without destroying the original in the process. So far, we haven't seen evidence that people are getting their body scanned or that their particles are getting destroyed at the quantum level when they die.

We're also not sure you *can* copy all your particles at the quantum level. Scanning all of the quantum states of a human body is no small feat, since there are 10^{28} particles, which dwarfs the total computer memory of human civilization, currently around 10^{21} bytes. Today, we could maybe store the information contained in one of your toenails if we used every computer in existence.

Of course, there is the possibility that this information could simply be available to whatever is executing your passage to the afterlife. Perhaps our universe is like a simulation running in another universe, in which case your information simply lives on a hard drive somewhere, ready to be read and copied.

The second question, "Does all your information get copied, or just part of it?" is a more philosophical question. For example, does the afterlife really need *all* the information in your body? Is it really important, for example, to know what every quark in your toenail is doing at the moment of your death?

Or could it be that the afterlife only needs part of your information? If so, which parts are needed?

We know that the arrangement of all your particles is what makes you unique, but it might be useful to think about what that arrangement does. Your arrangement of particles defines a biological machine, a set of mechanical processes at the cellular level that takes in information from the world and reacts to it with certain actions. Is the arrangement of quantum particles in your toes or even your limbs necessary for that? What about your gut? Do you still need your gut instincts in the afterlife?

It could be that what you actually need for the afterlife is not the arrangement of every particle in your body but just the *design* of your biological machine. Maybe what lives on is not the quantum information of all your cells but how those cells are connected to one another, and what information they have stored in your brain circuits. That would definitely help you save on hard drive space.

And you can imagine compressing your *you* information even further, ignoring more and more details like a fuzzy JPEG image of yourself. Would that *you* still be you, though? Or would it just be a simplification, like the "essence" of you?

Hey, at least you're not an animated GIF.

The last question, "Which version of you gets to go on?" is more of a timing question. Our bodies and our minds change a lot over our lives. While our conscious experience and knowledge get bigger as we age, our bodies and mental capacity peak and start to decrease at some point. Which version of you is the one that goes to the afterlife? In other words, when does the copying and pasting take place?

If it happens at the moment of your death, you might find something to complain about. What if you are not at your best when the moment happens? Or what if there are things that happen to you leading up to your death that you'd rather not carry with you to eternity? Who gets to choose, and how?

Or perhaps the process of capturing you for the afterlife happens on a curve. Maybe what gets copied is an average of you, or a sum total of what makes the JPEG image of you unique. If all we are is information, science knows a lot of tricks you can use to compress, average, or find the most important features of that information.

Don't move.

Existing in Another Location Forever

The last piece of the afterlife puzzle is the idea that your you-ness somehow lives on forever in another place. In some ideas of the afterlife, this place is among the clouds (or down below the earth). In other cases, it just exists as a separate realm, detached from our plane of existence.

This idea sounds fantastical, but the notion of multiple universes is something that physics actively considers. Whether that's at all plausible depends a lot on where this afterlife is located.

It could be that our universe is actually a subset of a larger "metauniverse," an idea physicists conceived to try to explain the origin of our universe. Physics has made some progress in understanding the rules of our universe, but we haven't made much progress in figuring out *why* our universe exists. One concept is that maybe our universe is just a bubble in a deeper, larger universe (the metauniverse), and that our space-time is just a fluke arising from special conditions but not fundamental in itself. In this case, going to the afterlife means that somehow our information gets scanned and copied to that outside universe.

Another possibility is that the afterlife is in a parallel universe. The idea of the "multiverse" in physics says that maybe our universe is not the only one, and that there could be other pockets of space-time elsewhere. In some theories, these other universes are alternate versions of ours, perhaps split through quantum decisions or through different initial conditions or even different laws of physics. If that's the case, there *could* be a version of our universe that is more ideal or utopian (a Shangri-la of sorts). At the same time, there could also be worse versions of our universe, full of fire and fury (a Hades of sorts). Somehow, our information would have to find a way to make it to these other universes, which is something that physicists currently don't think is possible.

Whatever the case, it's interesting to think that the rules of those other universes could be totally different from ours. What sort of adaptation would you have to make to your *you* information to exist in this universe? Would time and causality even work the same way? What sort of vessel or machine (biological or not) would your information sit on? After all, if the afterlife is forever, you also want to be able to think and change and experience things in your new universe home. You want *life* after death, not sitting around frozen forever. That means that the metauniverse would have to be able to run your software, whether through states of quantum objects or something else we can't imagine yet. Think of it as porting a human program over to a new kind of alien computer.

File extension not supported

Uh-oh.

Heaven on Earth

A final possibility is that maybe our universe *is* the metauniverse. It could be that the afterlife can exist within our universe, not outside or next to it.

For example, maybe some neighboring alien species has created a Valhalla for us, and is standing by with scanners ready to copy us into it when we die. Or even more interesting, it could be that *we* build an afterlife for ourselves.

How would this work? Well, we could develop the same kind of technology that we imagine some heavenly force might use to whisk us off.

For example, we could develop the technology to scan a full body down to the molecular or particle level (or at least the human-essence level), and we could also develop the bioengineering or 3D printing technology to build new bodies for ourselves. Those two technologies could be used to create new copies of ourselves that are younger or healthier, and they could be sent to exist in a different location. Maybe we could house them in a more idealized place, or a worse one, depending on why you made the afterlife.

Of course, we are very far from having the technology to do this, and there are also a few tricky quantum mechanical issues to consider, as we mentioned before. In that case, it might be easier to not have a physical body at all!

Instead of trying to re-create your body, you could take advantage of the fact that you are just information and live on in a *simulated* afterlife.

All of the essential information that makes you *you* could be uploaded into a computer, which would then run a simulation for your digital self. Your digital copy would exist in this environment and even grow and change within it. And since it's all made up, this afterlife could be specially tailored for you. Do you want fifty sundaes for breakfast every day? No problem! Do you want to live out your 1980s fantasy or hang out with Jon Hamm *Black Mirror–*style? In a digital world, anything is possible.

Would it last forever? Well, it would last as long as someone keeps the computers plugged in. Interestingly, you could set the time rate inside the simulation to whatever speed you like. Depending on how fast the computer processors are, you could spend a million lifetimes inside your digital afterlife in the time it takes the computer technician to go get a cup of coffee.

Our current computers are not powerful enough right now to store all of your information or mimic the world perfectly, but they are improving quickly, and it seems likely they'll be able to pull off a pretty sweet afterlife in the near future.

Loading rainbows...

Ripples Through Time

As you can see, heaven is no joke. To put on an afterlife requires nothing short of building entire universes, figuring out remote and spontaneous scanning of countless quantum particles, and finding a way to move all this information around without anyone ever noticing. While we can't technically rule it out, from a physics point of view it seems like a tall order.

In the end, all that physics can do is look at the world around us and draw conclusions from what we can test and observe. So far, our current view of the universe is that it follows strict rules. There seem to be no exceptions, no matter how much our minds would like it to be otherwise. To the best of our knowledge, there is no evidence that anything but entropy happens once we die.

Does that mean that physics gives a thumbs-down to an afterlife existing in our universe? That when we die, who we are is gone forever?

Not entirely.

According to quantum mechanics, quantum information can't be destroyed in this universe. What this means is that when your body dies, the particles it's made out of may separate and scatter, but their quantum information won't disappear. That quantum information will probably be absorbed or transformed into other particles, but it will never go away. It will stay encoded in the quantum state of the universe, like an imprint or a clue. Technically, someone in the distant future could examine that imprint and reconstruct who you are and what you did. Such is the power of quantum mechanics.

And this idea extends to your actions as well. Every action you take causes interactions with other particles, and changes their quantum state in a unique way that in principle stores the information of that interaction. In a very real sense, our actions ripple through time, never lost and always present in the quantum history of the universe.

In this way, everyone who ever lived is still with us, through the faint but indelible mark we all leave on the things around us. One day, you too may die, and you will become part of the universe's record. There's an old adage that says we live on in the hearts and minds of those who knew us. According to quantum mechanics, this isn't just true; it's a mathematical fact.

THE UNIVERSE REMEMBERS

Do We Live in a Computer Simulation?

s this really happening? For real?

That's a question that people often ask themselves whenever they're experiencing something great (or not so great), or sometimes even when they read the news these days. The world we live in can seem so outrageous or so mind-boggling that it's hard to believe it really exists.

Then again, maybe it doesn't!

An idea that has been around for thousands of years is that the universe we live in, the one we experience with all of our senses, might not actually be real. Ancient religions often talk about our world being nothing but an illusion, and Socrates wondered if we would even be able to tell the difference. More recently, Keanu Reeves summed it all up in *The Matrix* with a single word: "Whoa."

We grow up assuming that what we see and feel is what's really out there, and that the universe is full of physical things that are moving around and banging into one another to make the sights and sounds that we take in with our senses. It certainly *feels* real. But *feeling* real and *being* real are not necessarily the same thing. For example, dreams can feel real when they are happening, but that doesn't mean you were actually being chased down the street by a building-size cookie.

Surprisingly, the question of whether our universe is real is something that modern physics has started to wonder about. Could our world not actually be happening? Is it possible that what we experience is just some elaborate simulation of a universe cooked up in an impossibly vast and powerful computer? And most important, how would we know?

Why Even Consider This?

The idea that the world isn't real and that we are actually living inside of a simulation might sound crazy to you. How could our messy and ultra-detailed world possibly be generated by a computer? Even something as simple as a fly buzzing around your living room is dense with detail, from its tiny wings furiously beating on billions of air molecules to its glittering eyes reflecting your face in each of its facets. Could a computer simulate all of that?

Actually, yes. Computer graphics have become incredibly realistic. Compare the simplicity of the original *Toy Story* movie with the most recent sequel (*Toy Story 4?*), and you'll start to understand the huge leaps in computer technology that have been made in just a few years. Virtual reality and video games have also become shockingly sophisticated compared to the blocky polygons of early versions. The latest sports video games are so convincing that it's hard to tell without taking a closer look whether it's a simulated game or actual footage of a live event. The celebrations, frustrations, and tantrums are all there! Considering the rate of progress, it's not hard to imagine that one day it might be hard or even impossible to tell the difference between virtual reality and actual reality.

SO real!

Famously, some people even argue that it's *likely* that we are living in a simulation. As we see our technology improve, we start to imagine a future in which everyone is running a simulation of a universe in their home computers. And some even imagine that in those simulations there could be simulated people inside of them running *more* simulations (a simulation inside a simulation!). If you keep going, pretty soon there are way more simulations running around than there is an actual universe, and it makes you wonder: What are the chances that we are living in the *one* true universe, and not in one of the countless simulated ones? Statistically speaking, you would have to put your money on the idea that we are living in a video game.

Philosophically, there is another reason to suspect we might be living inside of a simulation: our universe seems to work *like* a simulation.

You see, our universe has a lot in common with the computer programs that we use to build virtual games and virtual worlds: it seems to follow rules.

The whole project of physics is to uncover the rules of the universe. And the universe does indeed seem to follow them. From quantum mechanics to general relativity, we seem to be inching closer to discovering the source code of the universe. But an often overlooked question is: Why does the universe follow rules anyway? Why is it so consistent and regular?

The laws of physics seem to work everywhere, all the time, in exactly the same way. It reminds you of . . . a computer program. Just like a piece of software, the universe we live in seems to be chugging along, blindly applying a set of instructions set down by a master programmer.

The fact that our universe has an awful lot in common with how you would expect a simulated universe to run is a fairly strong argument that it could be just that.

Is It Possible, Though?

What would it take to actually simulate an entire universe?

It's clear that programmers are accomplishing amazing things recently, but that doesn't mean it's now easy to build a virtual universe. It's a big leap from describing a simple fly in a single location to describing *everything*. It feels like an overwhelmingly impossible task because "everything" is a lot of things. Not only are there a lot of details in flies and blades of grass, but there are a whole lot of flies and zillions of blades of grass. And that's just on our planet!

To get a sense of what it would take, let's paint a picture of how a simulated universe might work. In our view, there are three basic ways in which it could happen.

Brain in a Vat

In one scenario, a computer is running the simulation and feeding messages to a real human brain. That brain is building its concept of the world from what it perceives through its senses. But those signals are not created by any sense organs in a real body but by the computer simulation. Inside the computer is a model of a whole fake universe that interacts with the brain. When the brain sends a message like "walk forward," the computer simulates the act of moving forward and computes how the world would change and what new inputs to give to the brain.

Alien Brain in a Vat

In a slightly wackier scenario, a computer could be running the simulation for an alien brain, and then pretending that the brain is actually human. The alien in the simulation might think that their brain is a blob of jelly filled with billions of neurons firing at each other, but really, it could be anything. Their actual brain could be much bigger, or smaller, or work on completely different principles, like a vast network of hydraulic pumps or tiny quantum computers or something even crazier.

You Are a Software Program

Prepare yourself for the deepest level of meta. What if we don't have a real brain at all? What if all the brains in the simulation are *also simulated*? In this scenario, all living and conscious minds are part of the larger program. The last few decades have seen huge leaps forward in artificial intelligence, and we are now capable of making computer systems that can mimic the brain's functions of learning and memory and solving problems. As these artificial minds get more complex, they accomplish things that humans confidently assumed AI could never do: defeat the world human chess champion, steer a car through traffic, identify faces, maintain a realistic conversation. It's not hard to imagine creating a virtual world with virtual intelligent beings running around inside of it.

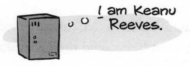

Of course, no matter what flavor of simulated universe you create, you'll still need a massive computer to make it work. To simulate a universe, you have to start with an initial setup: where all the objects are, and how fast they are moving. Then we apply the laws of the universe: What happens to those objects in the first moment? Do they bounce off one another, or pass through one another, or speed up or slow down or turn left? Each object is updated according to the rules, and time ticks one step forward. Then you repeat and see what happens.

This can take a lot of computing power if you have a lot of objects. For example, each object requires some computer memory to keep track of where it is and what it's doing. Now imagine how much memory you'd need for an entire universe, and how much processing power you'd need to crunch through all that data. You would have to simulate every particle and planet in the universe at the same level of incredible detail. Wouldn't that be impossible?

Maybe not. To be convincing, a simulated universe only has to seem real to the beings experiencing the simulation. Here are some ways in which you can get away with less computing power than you might think.

Shortcut #1

The first shortcut you can take is to make your simulated universe a simpler version of the actual universe. For example, you could build it with fewer dimensions than the real universe, or with simpler rules, or with more pixelation. Just because a simulated universe is simpler doesn't mean that it wouldn't seem real to the simulated creatures that live inside of it. It might be that our universe is very simple compared to the real universe, but we don't know any different, so we are happy with the realism that it provides. We could, for example, be like sentient characters in a Super Mario game, and think that this universe is as complex as it gets.

I think, therefore it's a-me, Mario!

Shortcut #2

You can also save on computer power by not making your simulation real-time. There are no rules that say that a simulation has to run at the same rate of time as the real rate outside the simulation.

For example, you could make your simulation run slower, so that one year inside the simulation actually takes one thousand years in the real universe. Then your computer would have enough time to render as much detail as you need to convince the beings inside of it that it's real. They wouldn't know the difference because that's the only time rate that they know. You could even pause the simulation, forget about it, and not restart it until the next day, and whatever is inside the simulation wouldn't notice. For example, do the characters in a video game notice when you've paused it to visit the bathroom? No, because they are *in* the game.

Shortcut #3

A third way to make a universe simulation possible is to be clever about the way you program it. Do you really have to simulate *all* the individual particles in the universe to fool its inhabitants into thinking that it's real? One common trick we use when writing simulations is to zoom in only when you need it. For example, when engineers simulate traffic patterns, they use cars as the building blocks and not the particles inside of each car. And when meteorologists write hurricane simulations, they start from clouds or water droplets, not protons.

In the same way, you could program a simulation of the universe in large chunks, like a rough version, and only go into the particle-level details when it's needed. Faraway planets would only be simulated if someone in the simulation builds a powerful enough telescope to see them, and individual particles would only be simulated when pesky simulated particle physicists build colliders to study them.

Could You Tell?

All of this is to say that it is entirely possible that we (or at least you)* could be living inside of a simulation. Technological trends point to it as a possibility, and philosophy tells us that a simulated universe would be just as valid to us as a real one. Does that mean that we are trapped in this limbo of not knowing? Is there any way to tell the difference between a real universe and a fake one?

It depends on how well the computer has been programmed. If it runs perfectly, then by definition it might be impossible to distinguish it from reality. It could be that the real universe outside of this one is vastly more complicated, and that building a computer powerful enough to simulate every detail that we experience is possible. In that case, we might never tell the difference.

But if computer programming in the real universe is *anything* like programming in our universe, then there is *always* a bug some-

---

* After all, it's possible that we are not real.

where. And that's our best chance to figure out whether our universe is a simulation: to find a glitch.

What would a glitch look like? It would depend on how the simulation is programmed, which makes it very difficult to predict. But we can make a few guesses!

It might be that the simulation has limits in its computing power. For example, it might have a hard time simulating things that happen across vast distances of space. When we build simulations of large, complex objects, we tend to simplify them by dividing them into smaller pieces. It's more feasible to simulate each piece separately and then stitch the results back together. A fake version of our universe might simulate each galaxy as a separate object, so that what happens inside one galaxy is independent of what's happening inside another galaxy. This is like taking a shortcut and hoping that it doesn't make a difference, because the beings in both galaxies are not likely to interact with each other.

But that only works if what happens in Andromeda stays in Andromeda. If there's something in the Andromeda Galaxy that can actually affect what happens in our galaxy, we could use that to try to find a glitch. For example, what if the supermassive black hole at the center of Andromeda is shooting particles at us that we can detect in our atmosphere? That would directly link the two galaxies, and the simulation might not get this right. There might, for example, be irregularities in the trajectory that the particles took to get here, or they might have inconsistent energies. Something like that might tell us there's something amiss in this universe.*

Another possibility is that the universe simulation could have limits in its resolution. Just like the old x86 computers were only able to render blocky, pixelated images in those black-and-green video monitors, it's possible that there is a minimum resolution that a fake universe can simulate. If we were to drill down into space and matter, and find that the universe is pixelated at a level that isn't explained by the laws of physics, that could be a sign that we are in a simulation.

One last possibility is that the simulation we're in could just not be well constructed. It happens all the time in programming here in our universe. As well-meaning or as careful as programmers can be, it seems that the simulations we make always break down at some point. Maybe there are cases that the programmers of our universe didn't account for, or loopholes that they didn't predict. The same thing could happen as we learn more and more about our

---

* In fact, physicists *do* see high-energy particles hitting our atmosphere that can't yet be explained by any astrophysical source.

universe. For example, we have two competing theories about the nature of reality (quantum mechanics and general relativity). Those two theories don't often interact, so they still seem to work on their own, but there are situations in which they totally contradict each other. One of these situations is inside of a black hole, where one theory predicts a singularity while another predicts a blob of uncertainty. It could be that whoever made our universe simulation didn't think the rules all the way through, and were either sloppy or lazy (or rushed) when they built it. Finding out that there is an inconsistency might tell us that there's something not quite right about this reality.

Why Build It?

The biggest question about this whole crazy notion of a simulated universe is, of course, "Why?"

Why would anyone (or anything?) go to all the trouble of creating a whole fake universe and populating it with either connected brains or artificial, sentient beings? Could they be mining us for energy, or enslaving us for some strange purpose?

It could be that our universe is an experiment of some sort. Maybe someone constructed our universe to try to answer a scientific question (such as "In how many universes do bananas evolve?"), or maybe a psychological one ("In how many of those universes are people smart enough to eat them?"). Or maybe we are an experiment for a certain type of universe, and there are countless other universe simulations in which the laws of physics are different, or even the nature of reality is different (that Super Mario world could be totally real in the next universe over).

Alternatively, maybe they're just doing it for fun. What if we're just the equivalent of a fishbowl in their universe, or a toy for their kids? Or worse, what if we're the screen saver in their mega-complex laptops? Who knows what anyone or anything smart enough to build a simulation as complex as our universe will find entertaining?

To summarize, it could be the case that we are all living inside of a simulated universe that runs like a giant machine, governed by rules that we are bound to follow and that we don't yet fully understand, with the possibility that we may never know the true nature of this reality. If this sounds a little grim, then think about the following question for a second: Is that any different than if we were in the real universe?

Maybe the real illusion is that there is a difference between a simulated universe and the real one. From a practical point of view, would it really affect your experience or your sense of self? Perhaps we should be happy to exist at all, simulated or not, and content with the quest to learn all the rules of our existence, whether or not we ever find the answers. If this *is* happening (even in a simulation), doesn't that make it real?

Why Does $E = mc^2$?

f there's one physics equation most people know, it's probably $E = mc^2$.

It's the most famous equation in physics, likely because it's easy to remember. Its form is simple and elegant, almost like the Nike "swoosh" logo. Compared to other physics formulas that look more like Egyptian hieroglyphics,* this one definitely has brand appeal. Of course, it doesn't hurt that it came from Einstein, whose

---

* One version of the Schrödinger equation, for example, looks like this:

$$i\hbar \frac{\partial}{\partial t} \Psi(\mathbf{r},t) = \left[\frac{-\hbar^2}{2\mu} \nabla^2 + V(\mathbf{r},t) \right] \Psi(\mathbf{r},t)$$

brilliance (and famous hairdo) have been a part of popular culture since the last century.

But physics formulas are not just math; they're supposed to describe something about the physical universe. And this is another reason why $E = mc^2$ sticks in people's minds. Here E stands for energy, m means mass, and c is the speed of light in a vacuum, or 299,792,458 meters per second. To have them all in a simple, easy-to-remember formula implies that they're connected to one another in a deep and profound way.

But what exactly does that mean? How are mass and energy and light actually related to one another? And what does this relationship say about the fundamental nature of ourselves and the universe?

Mass and Energy

For most of us, mass is the stuff we're made out of.

If something has mass, it generally means that it's heavy, hefty, substantial. We tend to think of things with less mass as lighter, ethereal, or barely there.

This is something we develop in our intuition at an early age, and it's something that was captured by Newton's laws of motion. For centuries, $F = ma$ held the top spot as the most important physics equation in the world. In this formula, F is the force that you apply to an object, m is the object's mass, and a is the acceleration, or how quickly the object starts to move. If the object has a lot of mass, then it takes a really big F to get the object moving. And if m is small, then a gentle push is enough to make it go.

To us, mass is a measure of the *substance* of something. Things with more mass, like mountains and planets, feel more real and solid.

On the other hand, we tend to think of energy as something completely different. We associate energy with heat, light, fire, or motion. It seems like something ephemeral that can flow or be transmitted. It gives you the power to do things and burn things. Like a magical quantity, it's something you can store and release when needed.

For a long time, this intuition about mass and energy fit quite neatly with Newton's laws and our basic understanding of the universe. Mass and energy were two different things, although it was clear they could interact with each other.

For example, if you added energy to something, like a cup of water, you could think about it speeding up the little water molecules in the cup, but not changing the mass of the water. After all, adding heat didn't change how many H_2O molecules there were; it just made them wiggle faster. At least, that's what we thought.

In the late 1880s, physicists started asking pesky questions, like "Where does mass actually come from?" and "What *is* it anyway?" Initially, they looked at the electron, which had just been discovered. Physicists noticed that when a charged particle (like the electron) moves, it makes a magnetic field. This magnetic field then pushes back on the particle, making it harder to get the particle moving faster. It's the same effect as if the electron had some kind of hard-to-push mass stuff to it, which gave physicists the first idea that mass and energy (in this case, the energy of the magnetic field) could be more than just two different things.

Then, Einstein stepped in with a clever argument that settled the debate.

At the time, Einstein had been preoccupied with the idea of *relativity*, the study of how the laws of physics apply to things that are moving relative to one another. It was known back then that nothing can move faster than the speed of light, and that this speed limit worked no matter how fast you were moving. If you were moving really fast, you would still see light moving at the speed of light. This fundamental limitation makes for some really strange effects when you consider how things look to someone standing on Earth and someone going really fast on a rocket ship.

For example, Einstein considered the case of a rock in space giving off heat. That heat will come off the rock in the form of infrared photons. If you are floating in space next to the rock, you might not notice anything strange. You would see photons coming off the rock and you would measure that the photons had a certain energy (as all photons do).

But if you were traveling past Earth on a speeding rocket ship, you would see something different. Einstein used the formulas of relativity to figure out that you would see the photons coming off the rock at a different frequency of light. This is an effect called the relativistic Doppler effect, which is similar to how, for example, a police siren sounds different if the police car is coming toward or away from you. In this case, though, the shift is a little stranger because of relativity rules (since you can't see the photon going faster or slower than the speed of light). The net effect is that you, in the spaceship, would measure the energy of the photons to be different than if you measured it when you're floating next to the rock. But since it's the same photons, something else must have changed.

According to Einstein, what also changed was the kinetic energy of the rock. But kinetic energy comes from the mass and the velocity of an object, and since the rock's velocity didn't change when it gave off photons, Einstein concluded that its mass must have changed. In fact, he found that the mass of the rock changed by an amount equal to the energy of the photons, if you multiplied it by the speed of light squared. In other words, he found the following:

Energy of the photon = (Change in mass of the rock) x (speed of light)²

   What this means is that when a photon leaves the rock, it actually changes the mass of the rock. This change in mass is the same (if you multiply it by the speed of light squared) as the energy of the photon emitted. It seems that a little bit of the mass of the rock was transformed into energy, which then went off in the form of a photon (remember that photons don't have any mass; they are pure energy).

This was a pretty groundbreaking result, to say the least. It threw out thousands of years of human intuition that told us that mass and energy were totally different things. Instead, Einstein's equation says that the two things are related to each other and that you can somehow transform one to the other in the same way that you can walk into a currency store and trade dollars for euros.

At this point, you might be wondering: What does this mean? How exactly can something like mass, which has substance, be transformed into pure energy and vice versa?

Initially, you might think that a few of the rock atoms somehow disintegrated and became these photons. That would be one way for the mass of the whole rock to decrease. But actually, this is not what happens at all. The rock has the same number of atoms before and after the photon is created, but somehow, the mass of the rock decreases.

This is very strange to us because we're not used to the mass of things changing. If you have a metal weight on your desk, you don't expect that weight to be lighter or heavier just because you turn the air-conditioning on or off. A pound of sugar is a pound of sugar, regardless of whether or not you put it in the fridge, right?

To understand what's really going on here, we have to dig a little deeper into what it means for something to have mass. In particular, there are two important clues that will help us put this puzzle together.

Most of Your Mass Isn't Stuff

You probably think of yourself as being made of solid "stuff." After all, you are what you eat, and you eat stuff. Not lightning or sunbeams. And when you poke your finger against your arm, it feels pretty solid.

But actually, if you look closer and zoom into the bits that make you up, you'll see that there's really not much there at all. If you look at any particular atom in your body, a lot of it is empty space. Almost all of the mass of the atom is found in the nucleus, since the proton and neutron each weigh two thousand times as much as the electron. And as we saw in Is an Afterlife Possible?, even more fascinating is that when we crack open a proton or neutron, we see that they are actually made of "up" and "down" quarks: two up quarks and a down for the proton, and two down quarks and an up for the neutron.

Atom   Protons   Quarks
        & Neutrons

So really, most of the mass in your body is in those groups of quarks. But what's really interesting is what happens when you separate those quarks.

If you measure the mass of the three quarks together (in the proton, for example), you will find that they have a mass of about 938 MeV/c² (one MeV/c² is about 1.7 x 10–30 kilograms).

But if you break open that proton and separate the three quarks, you will find that each up quark only has a mass of about 2 MeV/c^2 and that the down quark only has a mass of 4.8 MeV/c^2.

The quarks hardly have any mass by themselves! They each weigh less than 1 percent of the mass of the proton.

And yet when you put the quarks together, somehow their mass increases by a factor of one hundred. That's like putting three Lego pieces together and then finding that all of a sudden they weigh as much as *three hundred* Lego pieces. What's going on? Where does all this mass come from?

The surprising answer is that the mass comes from the energy that ties the quarks together.

You see, one amazing fact we've learned is that energy acts like mass. If you have a bit of energy in one spot—say, trapped in the bonds between two particles—that little bit of energy will be hard to push and pull in the same way that mass is hard to push and pull. If you separate the two particles and let the energy dissipate, then the particles will be easier to move around. In other words, energy itself has inertia.

And not only that, energy also feels gravity. Any little bit of trapped energy will also bend space and get attracted to other objects, just like things with mass do.

So in the case of the proton, its mass is the sum of the individual masses of the three quarks, *plus* the energy of the bonds that hold them together (for quarks, it's the strong nuclear force that binds them).

This is true for all things in nature, not just protons. The mass of, say, a llama is equal to the mass of all its particles plus the energy needed to keep all those particles together (including the regular chemical bonds between the molecules). If you were to split the llama in two (sorry, llama), the sum of the masses of the two pieces would be less than the mass of the original llama.

And how do we figure out what the equivalent energy of that lost mass is? You guessed it: we use $E = mc^2$.

This is partly what $E = mc^2$ means: that mass is equivalent to energy. And it turns out that most of what we consider to be our mass (about 99 percent) is actually just energy.

The Other 1 Percent

What about the other 1 percent of us? That's still *stuff*, right? Actually, not so much.

In the last hundred years, we've also learned a lot about the nature of the mass of the fundamental particles. We've looked as closely as we can, and so far, particles like quarks and the electron don't look like they are made of smaller pieces. This tells us that their mass doesn't come from the energy of holding smaller bits together. So where does their mass come from?

The original idea from the 1880s was actually on the right track. Electrons are harder to move because of the magnetic field that they generate. But there's another field out there that also pushes back at them: the Higgs field. Filling the universe, this quantum field tugs at all of the matter particles, making them harder to move. This is where the mass of each particle comes from. It's each particle's interaction with the Higgs field. But that's only a partial explanation.

I feel so... massive...

The full explanation is that the mass comes from the *energy* of the Higgs field. Some particles interact a lot with the energy stored in the Higgs field, which makes them harder to move. And some particles have weaker interactions, which makes them easier to move. In other words, the mass of each particle is really just the strength of its connection to the energy of the Higgs field.

And we can go a step further still. According to quantum theory, quarks and electrons themselves are nothing more than little ripples of energy in the quantum fields that permeate the universe. A particle is just a burst of energy, in the same way that a shout is a ripple in the air, or an ocean wave is a ripple in water. In other words, even the particles themselves are just energy!

A Massive Conclusion

Both of these clues—that most of the mass of an object is the energy of the bonds that hold that object together, and that even the mass of each particle is really just energy—lead us to an amazing, and somewhat shocking, conclusion: what we thought of as "mass" doesn't really exist. It's all just energy.

This is how the rock in space is able to lose mass when it radiates a photon. It doesn't lose mass because it transformed matter into energy. All matter is already energy. The rock just transformed energy from one form to another. In this case, it transformed the energy in the motion or vibration of the molecules into a photon.

So when you think of the rock in space, don't think of it as having mass *and* energy. Just think of it as one big blob of collected energy. Some of that energy is in the particles, some of it is in the bonds between the particles, and some of it is in the motion of the particles, but it's all just one pool of energy.

The reverse can also happen: if the rock absorbs a ray of sunlight and heats up, it adds to the pool of energy. And more energy means that the rock will be harder to move and that it will weigh more due to gravity. This means that hot rocks really *are* more massive than cold rocks. Of course, the difference is small: remember that to calculate the equivalent mass change, you have to divide the energy of the photon by the speed of light squared, which is a big number.

This is what $E = mc^2$ reveals: that mass is equivalent to energy. These days, physicists say that mass is a *form* of energy. This is because there are other forms of energy. For example, photons can have energy but not mass.

Just Do It

The famous formula does tell us that there's a deep connection between mass and energy. But it's not that mass is something that can be transformed into energy. What we've learned is that all mass is just energy. It's the energy of the particles of an object, either in their bonds with one another or in their interaction with the Higgs field.

The idea that energy has inertia or that it weighs something feels odd and counterintuitive, but that's only because we've been thinking about mass the wrong way for hundreds of years. There is no such thing as "stuff"; there's only energy and the impact it has on the shape of space (gravity) and how things move (inertia). Those are the two sides of Einstein's two-part relativity tango.

Fundamentally, this changes how we look at the universe. We no longer see the universe as filled with matter and energy. The entire universe is just energy, including us. In a real way, we are luminous beings made of energy.

Just don't expect to shoot lasers from your eyes anytime soon.

Where Is the Center of the Universe?

The center of anything is an important place.

For example, the center of your city is a landmark. It's where most of the action is, like where the best bakeries are and where important decisions are made. The very center of the city is also usually the oldest part, where the first loaf was baked and the first house was built.

YE OLDE BAKERY

The same is true, on a really large scale, for a lot of things in space. Our solar system has a center: the Sun! It's the first thing that formed out of the cloud of gas and dust that made us, and it's still the densest spot. It's also the best source of light and energy, and it's definitely the busiest place in the solar system: the lights never go out on the Sun. Even our galaxy has a center—a supermassive black hole with the mass of millions of stars whose gravity helps keep everything in place.

But centers are also important because they give you a sense of place. They help orient your location and give you a hint about where you are relative to everything else. Without knowing that, you might feel a little unmoored or lost, like being out at sea without a compass or getting stuck inside an IKEA store.

So what about the whole universe? Does it have a center, where everything started and where all the important universe business happens? And if it does, how close or far are we from it? Do we live near the center of the action or are we out in the middle of nowhere, cosmically speaking?

Let's take a look around and see if we can pinpoint the center of, well, *everything*. Who knows, we might even find some action when we get there.

What Can We See?

You can usually find the center of a city by looking at a map. Unfortunately, we don't have a map of the whole universe, because we can't see all of it. This is not because there's something blocking our view, or because the universe is too big, but because the speed of light is just too darn slow.

While light is pretty fast compared to competitive IKEA shoppers and airplanes, it's not infinitely fast. It takes time to cross the zillions of miles of space to bring us images of the distant reaches of the universe. And unfortunately, the universe is too young for us to see all of it. Physicists believe the universe started fourteen billion years ago, which puts a limit on the photons that we can see. If something is so far away that its light would take longer than fourteen billion years to reach us, then we can't see it. That means that the farthest thing we can see is something that sent light in our direction just after the universe started. Anything farther than that, and not enough time has passed for the light to get here, though it's on its way.

This volume of space that we can see is something we call the "observable universe." And since light travels at the same speed in all directions, this volume is a sphere centered around you (or more accurately, your eyeballs).

To be sure, the observable universe is huge. Because the universe is expanding, it's actually bigger than 14 billion light-years in every direction. Objects whose light is arriving now after 14 billion years are actually even farther away now because space got bigger. This expansion of space has stretched our field of view up to around 46.5 billion light-years, making the observable universe 93 billion light-years wide. And if we were looking for the center of the observable universe, the answer would be simple: it's you. We are each at the center of our own observable universe, since we all receive photons at a slightly different location.

And in fact, each person's observable universe is growing every year. Not just because space is still expanding but because as time passes, more photons are able to reach us, letting us see things that are farther and farther away.

But of course, the observable universe is not the same thing as the actual universe. Our limited view doesn't necessarily tell us whether the universe has a center. It could be that the observable universe is almost the same size as the actual universe, in which case we might start to get a sense of where the center is soon. Or it could be that the universe is much bigger than what we can see, and our little bubble of vision is off in a sad corner, missing all the fun.

Guess there's not much going on in the Universe.

Hints from the Structure of the Universe

Even though we can technically see to the edge of the observable universe, we've only just started to look around and figure out what's in our neighborhood. Only recently have we been able to build telescopes powerful enough to get a closer look at those far-away and dim galaxies.

And when we look around, the first thing we discover is that stars and galaxies are not evenly spread out across the universe, like chocolate chips in a well-baked muffin. Instead, they are arranged in large structures that gravity has managed to put together after fourteen billion years of patient work.

Our galaxy is part of a little cluster of neighborhood galaxies called the "Local Group." The galaxies orbit a common central point, swooshing around in space and occasionally running into one another. Our neighbor, Andromeda, will crash into our galaxy in about five billion years. There are other similar galactic clusters nearby, and together we all form a supercluster of galaxies that's many millions of light-years wide.

But superclusters like ours are not the biggest thing in the universe. In the last decades our telescopes have revealed that superclusters form even bigger structures: the walls of enormous bubbles that encase billions of cubic light-years of *nothing*. We are still putting together the whole picture, but as far as we know, those bubbles are the biggest structures in the universe.

Does that tell us where the center of the universe is? It would be great if the structure that we see told us something about where the center might be. Maybe we could see a pattern, like the way build-

Galaxy   Super   Super Cluster
            Cluster   Bubbles

ings tend to get bigger as you get closer to downtown, or how galaxies get more crowded near their middle.

Unfortunately, not even these giant bubbles tell us much about where a center could be. They seem to keep going in every direction quite evenly. It doesn't get denser on any particular side or suggest any kind of pattern to find the center.

Hints from the Movements of Galaxies

Another way we might be able to find the center of the universe is to look at how all those galaxies and superclusters are moving. After all, we can tell where the center of the solar system is just by looking at the trajectories of all the planets. In the same way, you can trace the center of a galaxy by looking at the paths of all the stars in it.

It turns out that everything we see in the universe is also moving. In fact, we think stuff has been shooting through space since the very first moment: the Big Bang. Could the motion of all the things in the universe tell us where the center of the universe is?

Most people imagine the Big Bang as an explosion. They think that all the stuff in the universe was crunched into a tiny dot, and then it all exploded out through space. So if we look at the direction everything is headed and run the clock backward, would that tell us where the center of the explosion was? Can we triangulate the Big Bang to find the center of the universe?

To try to figure this out, we have measured the velocity of many of the galaxies we can see. We do this by looking at the color of the light they shine at us. Just like a police siren sounds different moving toward you or away from you, the light from galaxies changes frequency if the galaxies are moving. Galaxies moving away from us look redder, while galaxies moving toward us look bluer.

And what do we see? We see that galaxies are indeed moving, and they're doing it at different speeds. But then we noticed something surprising: the motion of all the galaxies tells us that they're all moving away from . . . us!

Does that mean that *we* are at the center of the universe? Did the Big Bang happen *in this spot*, and now everything is flying away from it?

Not exactly. You see, the Big Bang wasn't actually an explosion; it was more of an *expansion* of space.

What's the difference? When a bomb explodes, it pushes everything away from the center. All of the bits of debris move away from a single point, and if you reverse their path, they would point back to the origin. That's why it's easy to tell where a bomb exploded. All you have to do is trace where all the debris came from.

But an expansion happens *at every point*, not from one center. It's more like a loaf of bread rising in the oven. It doesn't just grow from the center, pushing outward. The little air bubbles in every part of the dough all grow at the same time, puffing up the loaf evenly. And if you were inside the expanding loaf, you would see every part of the bread moving away from you, regardless of where you were. And that explains why we see things moving away from us in every direction: you would see that no matter where you are in an expanding universe.

THE UNIVERSE RISES

Unfortunately, that also means we can't use the expansion of the universe to tell where the center of everything is. Like an expanding loaf, all we know is that the universe is growing everywhere, so the center could be here or it could be anywhere.

And sadly, we also can't tell where the center is from the motion of the bubbles and superclusters. It would be great if they were all moving in orbit around a central spot, but so far it doesn't appear that they do.

Finding the Crust of the Universe

Does all of this mean that we will never find the center of the universe? Not necessarily.

Some of you might be thinking that just because a loaf of bread is expanding everywhere doesn't mean that it doesn't have a center. And you would be right. A loaf of bread is both expanding at every point *and* it can have a center. But it depends on the shape of the loaf.

One way to define a center is by geometry. For the bread, this is the point in the loaf where there's the same amount of bread in every direction. You can figure this out by tracing out where all the edges of the bread are (i.e., its crust) and then finding the middle point of all those edges.

BREAD JOKES NEVER
GET STALE

Could we find the center of the universe in the same way? Sure, but that depends on whether the universe even *has* a shape!

The problem is that we just don't know if the universe has a crust like a loaf of bread. We can't tell what's beyond the edge of the observable universe because we can't see that far. But there are a few possibilities.

The Universe Has a Blobby Shape

If the universe does have a shape, it *could* look like a loaf of bread, in which case it would have a center. It could be that this center is important, like maybe it contains some of the earliest matter that formed in the Big Bang, or maybe it technically occupies the spot where the rest of the universe came from. But it could also be that this center isn't very special. Maybe it's just the place that happens to be right in the middle. For example, take Oklahoma: it's right in the center of the United States, but few people would consider it especially important (sorry, Oklahoma).

The Universe Is Infinite

It could also be that the universe continues to do its thing, filling space with bubbles of galaxy superclusters forever. Forever is a hard concept to grasp, but it means that you can travel in any particular direction and you would never run out of universe. This might sound strange, but a lot of physicists say that an infinite universe makes more sense that a finite one. And if it's true that the universe is infinite, it would mean something shocking: *the universe has no center.* If you define the center to be the point where there's the same amount of stuff in every direction, then every point in an infinite universe satisfies that definition, because there's infinite stuff in every direction.

The Universe Has a Funny Shape

The final possibility is that the universe has a finite shape, but that shape can defy having a center. How is that possible? Well, it turns out that space can bend, so it doesn't always go in a straight line. This means that you can shape space in all kinds of interesting ways. For example, it could be that the universe curves back on itself, just like the surface of Earth curves around. If that's the case, then where is its center? Just like Earth's surface doesn't have a center (still not you, Oklahoma), the universe could also avoid having one. It could also be that the universe curves in a weird way, like in the shape of a donut. In that case, the universe would have a center, but that center wouldn't be inside the universe!

The Holey Center

While it doesn't seem likely that we'll ever travel far enough to personally check whether the universe has a crust, or whether it's infinite or shaped like a donut, it might still be possible to know which of these possibilities is true. By studying the nature of space and looking at its curvature around us, we might one day be able to infer what the overall shape of space is. It might tell us whether it goes on forever or loops around, or it might point us in the general direction of a geometric center.

The Central Point

Unfortunately, we don't currently know where the center of the universe is, and we might never know. We don't even know if the universe *has* a center!

But regardless of whether there's a center to the universe or not, there is a silver lining. We know for sure that the universe is expanding everywhere. And we also know that the Big Bang was not an explosion into empty space but an expansion of space itself. In a way, this tells us that everywhere is equally important, and that no place in the universe is more special than any other place. Like the loaf of bread, every point in the universe is the site of new space being created, which means that every point is the center of its own little universe.

For a physicist, that scenario feels more natural because the laws of physics shouldn't favor any one point over another. If there was a center, then physicists would ask, "Why that point?" and "Why not some other point?" It's much simpler to assume a democratic universe.

So in the end maybe we don't need to know where the center of the universe is. Each of us could just be content with being the center of our own observable universe, mooring ourselves to other people's view of the universe, and growing our awareness and perception of it as it continues to expand (perhaps infinitely) in all directions.

THE UNIVERSE: YOU
GOTTA LOAF IT.

PS: For bonus homework, go to Google Maps, search for "center of the universe," and then zoom out to see where it is.

Can We Turn
Mars into Earth?

E arth is pretty great, right? It offers incredible views, tasty street food, and good schools. As long as we take care of it, humans should be able to live comfortably on it for a long time.

But is Earth the only planet that we can live in? Unfortunately, looking around our solar system, there aren't any other options that have the same luxury amenities, or even basic things like reasonable temperatures, a breathable atmosphere, or liquid water on the surface.

Even if we found another planet like Earth out there, traveling to it would take dozens, hundreds, or thousands of years, unless we invent warp drives or find a way to manipulate wormholes. Instead, what if we found a fixer-upper closer to home? One that might need some work and a coat of paint, but that we could travel to without spending decades crammed inside a smelly colony ship?

Well, look no further than the planet that is literally next door: Mars! It needs a bit of work and updated bathroom fixtures, but it has real potential. And it scores very highly in the three most important categories: location, location, and location.

What would it take to give Mars a makeover? And can we make it as nice as Earth?

Living on Mars

When we say that we'd like to make Mars livable, we mean that we'd like it to be as similar to Earth as possible. We could, in theory, build space stations to live there, where you have to wear a fancy suit to go outside. You could even build massive domes to enclose cities and stay indoors the whole time. But what kind of life would that be?

To really call a place home, we want to be able to roam free, breathe fresh air in green parks, and enjoy the land. We don't want to have to wear space suits to go for a walk, or slather on 1000 SPF lotion to avoid cosmic radiation.

The problem is that Mars isn't quite in move-in condition. To make Mars more like Earth, we'd need to change several things about it that make it a not-so-nice place to live in right now:

◆ There's no liquid water on the surface.

◆ It's very cold there (think Antarctica all year round).

◆ There's no breathable atmosphere.

◆ The surface is bombarded by harmful cosmic rays.

Let's tackle each of these one at a time.

Water, Water Everywhere

Everyone knows that water is connected to life. Not only does all life (as we know it) need water to survive but we think that life started in the water. When we look around the solar system for possibilities of alien life, one of the first questions we ask is: Where is there liquid water? So far, Earth is the only place in the solar system where we have found liquid water on the surface. And that's what we want: easily accessible liquid water, preferably in beautiful lakes and running streams.

Of course, "liquid" is the key term here, because water as a molecule is not actually that rare in the solar system. In fact, Uranus and Neptune are called "ice giants" because they have so much solid water. The dwarf planet Ceres is estimated to be half ice, and a lot of the rocks in the asteroid belt are basically huge dirty snowballs. In fact, scientists think that much of the water on Earth came from the far reaches of the solar system. A young, hot Earth boiled away a lot of its original water into space, but its water was later replenished by impacts from comets and other icy space rocks. That's right, our oceans are *filled* with melted cosmic snowballs. The next time you drink a glass of water, remember you're enjoying a cool, refreshing glass of melted comet.

NEW BUSINESS IDEA

Mars definitely doesn't have any surface oceans, but it still has plenty of frozen water aboveground and liquid water deep underground. Mars, like Earth, is colder at its north and south poles than at its equator. And its poles are covered in ice, just like those on Earth. Lots of ice. So much ice that if you could melt all of it, Mars would be covered in water to a depth of one hundred feet. That's plenty of water for future humans living there to drink, swim, and build waterslides for their theme parks.

If we want oceans and rivers in our new home, all we have to do is melt it and keep it melted. But that's tricky because Mars is very, very cold on its surface, and it has a very thin atmosphere. Any liquid water out in the open is most likely going to freeze, or boil into vapor in the vacuum of space.

The good news is that if we can figure out a way to heat up Mars, and also find a way to give it an atmosphere, then Mars can have liquid lakes and oceans and be one step closer to resembling our dear planet Earth.

Making Mars Toasty

From the look of it, you might imagine that the surface of Mars is toasty and warm. It shines red, after all, and it mostly looks like a desert. But Mars is actually very cold. Its red color comes from all the oxidized iron in its soil. The average temperature on Mars is −81°F, which is much colder than the temperature on Earth's South Pole.

If we want to turn up the thermostat on Mars and make it a cozier place to live, we need to think about what gives a planet its temperature. A planet's surface temperature is mainly set by two basic things:

(a) How much heat it gets from the Sun

(b) How much of that heat it holds on to

Most of the heat in the solar system comes from the Sun, so the amount of heat a planet gets depends on where it is in the solar system. The closer a planet is to the Sun, the more heat it gets. Mars gets a decent amount of heat, since it is the fourth-closest planet to the Sun. But it doesn't get as much as Earth, which is one planet closer.

One potential solution is to change the distance between Mars and the Sun. We could build giant planet-size rockets and strap them to Mars to steer it to a closer orbit. A cheaper but more dangerous idea would be to use another heavy rock as a gravitational tugboat. If we could steal a big asteroid and put it in orbit near Mars, the gravitational effects could pull Mars in the right direction. Assuming, of course, that we don't slam that asteroid into the planet.

If that sounds a bit crazy, then maybe we should consider other promising solutions. For example, we could increase the temperature of Mars by helping it keep more of the energy it gets from the Sun. Planets don't wear puffy down vests or parkas to stay warm, but they do have atmospheres. Atmospheres aren't just great for breathing and giving you beautiful sunsets; they can also act like jackets to planets, thanks to the greenhouse effect.

ATMOSPHERES: ALWAYS
A HOT ACCESSORY

When light from the Sun hits a planet, it heats up the rocks and mountains and all the things on the planet surface. When these things warm up, they glow in the infrared.* Normally, this energy would just radiate out into space and get lost. But if you have an atmosphere, that radiation can get trapped inside. The key is to have carbon dioxide (CO_2) in your atmosphere.

CO_2 works like a one-way mirror because it only absorbs a particular kind of light: the infrared kind. Visible light from the Sun

---

* That's just because Earth and Mars are cooler than the Sun. Everything in the universe glows at a wavelength determined by its temperature. The Sun glows in the visible spectrum, and planets like Earth glow in the infrared.

passes through the CO_2 on its way in, but when that light gets reflected back as infrared, it gets blocked by the layer of CO_2, trapping the energy inside and warming up the planet. Of course, you can imagine how having too much CO_2 can cause your planet to overheat, too.

Mars does have an atmosphere, and most of it (about 95 percent) is CO_2. Sadly, though, Mars's atmosphere is pretty thin. In terms of pressure, Mars's atmosphere is less than 1/100th the pressure of Earth's. So most of the sunlight that falls on Mars just gets radiated back out into space.

We could bring Mars up to a warmer temperature by engineering a massive atmospheric makeover and increasing the amount of CO_2 in the atmosphere. But to get that full greenhouse effect, Mars would actually need more CO_2 than we have in our atmosphere on Earth, since Mars gets less sunlight than we do. So where do we get more CO_2?

Until recently, most of the CO_2 on Earth came from volcanic eruptions. But Mars doesn't have any active volcanoes that can spew out CO_2. The interior of Mars is cold and hard, without the flowing rivers of molten lava that powers volcanoes. Scientists think that millions of years ago it was a different story, and Mars was hot and melty on the inside. But Mars is smaller than Earth—about half of its diameter—so it cooled and hardened faster than Earth, like a smaller cup of coffee on a winter morning.

One little bit of good news is that Mars already has a small source of CO_2 that we could use. Those layers of ice at the poles are not all made of frozen water. A lot of that ice is actually frozen CO_2. Yes! That's just what we need. If we could somehow melt the poles, we would unlock plenty of water, and release a little bit of CO_2 to help keep it warm.

Unfortunately, even if you released *all* of the CO_2 on the poles, you would only get about 1/50th of the CO_2 you'd need to keep the planet warm and toasty.

Are there other sources of CO_2 we could find? Actually, the solar system has plenty of frozen CO_2 in asteroids and comets. One potential solution is to send spaceships to nudge some comets and get them to smash into the surface of Mars.* It would take a *lot* of comets, probably thousands or millions of them.

Before you start building your fleet of comet-steering spaceships, there's another issue. The amount of CO_2 you need to keep Mars warm would unfortunately also make the air poisonous for humans to breathe. We can tolerate a bit of CO_2 in our lungs, but if

---

* Probably best to do that *before* we send people over.

you have too much, you start to feel drowsy, get headaches, sustain brain damage, and eventually die. Unfortunately, there's no happy ending to blanketing Mars with more CO_2.

There is another way to heat up the planet, though. We could capture more of the Sun's rays and direct them to the surface of Mars by using huge space mirrors. How huge? To gather enough light to warm up Mars, we would need space mirrors *the size of Mars*. That's not a small project. But it would provide the heat we need to release the CO_2 and water at the poles and make Mars both warmer and wetter.

Oh Yeah, Oxygen

If we manage to get the air temperature just right and melt the ice in the Martian polar regions to make new rivers and lakes, we still have a lot of work to do to make Mars into a capable replacement for Earth. We need to be able to breathe the air. Specifically, we need oxygen! Nobody wants to strap on a breathing mask every time they go for a picnic or borrow a cup of flour from the neighbors.

While oxygen is very common in the solar system, the kind that we need to breathe is surprisingly hard to find. Human lungs need the oxygen molecule O_2, which is a pair of oxygen atoms tied together. There is plenty of oxygen in the universe; it's one of the lighter elements, so it's made in vast quantities by the fusion at the heart of stars. But oxygen is a very friendly atom, and likes to bond with basically everything else around it. On Mars, there's oxygen in water (H_2O) and in carbon dioxide (CO_2), but almost no pure O_2.

On Earth, our air is around one-fifth O_2. In our case, it wasn't made geologically but as the byproduct of early life. Most of the original O_2 on Earth was produced by tiny little organisms in the ocean. These early bacteria were doing photosynthesis long before there were even plants. Around 2.5 billion years ago, those little organisms drank sunlight and water and CO_2 and burped out O_2 in the process. There wasn't any oxygen-breathing life at the time, so the amount of oxygen steadily increased for millions of years (maybe even a billion). Later, these microorganisms were incorpo-

Great, first comet water and now bacteria farts?

rated into plants, which continue to pump out the O_2 we need to breathe.

Could we somehow make this happen on Mars? It sounds promising: a little biological machine that will use the sunshine and the newly melted water and CO_2-rich atmosphere to create O_2 for us. Even better, these organisms multiply on their own, so we just have to plant a few batches of them on Mars and they will make more of themselves. It's like crowdsourcing on a whole new level, and we can pay for it with sunshine.

As usual, though, there's a catch. On Earth, this process took a long time, maybe a billion years. That wasn't inconvenient for us because it started long before humans existed. If we had kicked off this project on Mars a billion years ago, it would be ready for us just about now. Short of building a time machine, are we doomed to wait a billion years for Mars to have a breathable atmosphere? Microbiologists have lots of tricks to make bacteria grow faster and work harder (and take shorter lunch breaks). But it's still a very big job for tiny little organisms, and even the sped-up version of this process will likely take many thousands or even millions of years.

How else can we fill Mars with oxygen? One solution is to build oxygen factories, which produce O_2 chemically instead of biologically. It might sound like science fiction, but actually, an early prototype of this device is on its way to Mars right now, as part of the Mars 2020 mission. NASA has made these machines mainly to make O_2 as rocket fuel for missions that will return samples from Mars, but in principle the same concept could be used to make breathable oxygen.

It's like pollution, but good.

Magnetic Field

Once you have spent billions of dollars producing a nice atmosphere (or enslaved zillions of bacteria to do it for you), you probably want it to stick around. It would be an epic fail if your atmosphere just got blown away, like cosmic dandelion fluff.

If you're thinking that's impossible because there's no wind in space to blow the atmosphere away, then let us introduce you to a whole different kind of wind. The "solar wind" is made of fast-moving particles from the Sun. It's mostly protons and electrons made in the same reactions that make all that beautiful sunlight. And there are also particles coming from deep space called "cosmic rays." None of these particles are harmless. Quite the opposite, actually, as they are fairly deadly. Astronauts in space have to wear heavy shielding to protect themselves from this harmful radiation. This stream of high-speed, tiny bullets will strip any planet of its atmosphere given enough time.

Thankfully, we have an awesome planetary protection system here on Earth: our magnetic field. When electrons or protons hit a magnetic field, they get deflected. Our magnetic field deflects many of the Sun's harmful particles, making them miss Earth or spiral up to the poles, where they create the dazzling northern and southern

Shields up!

lights. Without our magnetic field, we would be blasted by harmful solar radiation, which would also strip away our atmosphere.

Unfortunately, Mars doesn't have a planetary magnetic field like Earth's. On Earth, our magnetic field is created by the rivers of molten metal flowing within our planet. Mars, however, is a smaller planet, and it has cooled earlier than Earth, which froze its inner core and killed its magnetic field. Without that magnetic field, anyone on the surface of Mars will need serious protection from radiation—thick suits lined with lead. That's not something you want to have to put on every time you go outside to kick a ball around with your Martian kids ("Mom, I have to pee . . ."). And without that magnetic field, any atmosphere you create will eventually get blown away. This is a bigger problem on Mars than on Earth because Mars has weaker gravity, so it's harder to keep the air molecules on its surface.

We could potentially restart Mars's magnetic field by heating the core and getting those metals flowing again, but jump-starting a whole planet is engineering on a scale even we can't imagine.

There is hope, though. Maybe we can build something that does the same job. Engineers at NASA came up with the clever idea of building an artificial magnetic shield, but instead of trying to wrap it around the whole planet, they suggest a smaller shield that is close to the Sun. Being close to the Sun lets the shield cast a larger magnetic "shadow." The shield would sit in space between the Sun and Mars, deflecting much of the solar wind to protect the atmosphere from getting blown away.

Other Homes?

This might all strike you as a lot of work. To summarize, turning Mars into a planet like Earth would require:

- ◆ A massive set of solar mirrors to focus sunlight and warm the planet

- ◆ A vast array of planetary factories to generate oxygen for us to breathe

- ◆ A space-based magnetic shield to protect the new Martians and their atmosphere from solar radiation

Perhaps you are thinking that Venus or the moon, which are also close by, would be better candidates.

Unfortunately, Venus has the opposite problems as Mars. The surface is blanketed with huge amounts of CO_2, which poison the air and trap heat. And since Venus is closer to the Sun than Earth, it gets more sunlight, which raises its surface temperature to a toasty 460°F. All that trapped energy also makes the atmospheric pressure at the planet surface so great that spacecraft landers we've sent to Venus have only survived a few minutes before being crushed to bits.

Of course, this hasn't stopped some wild-thinking scientists from proposing wacky ideas: What if you scooped the CO_2 out of Venus (using giant spoons?) and used space mirrors to deflect some of the sunlight? Would that make Venus habitable? Others have suggested building cloud cities that would float fifty kilometers above the surface of Venus. At that level, the temperature and pressure are actually similar to those of Earth. Sadly, those clouds are made of sulfuric acid, which makes writing the ad copy for the real estate brochures a little tricky ("Live on Venus! The views will take your breath away . . . literally!").

MY GENIUS IDEA

The moon is even closer, but frankly, it's just not big enough. Its mass is about 1 percent of the mass of Earth, which gives it such weak gravity that it can't hold on to any atmosphere. The individual particles of air would routinely shoot off into space, so even if we imported the ingredients from Earth, it would all disappear within a hundred years.

So in the neighborhood, Mars really is the best bet.

Should We Move?

Mars might be our best prospect for a second home world, but it's definitely a serious renovation project. Making Mars habitable would probably cost trillions and trillions of dollars, and might take thousands of years. And that's the *initial* estimate. Contractors always find a way to charge you extras once they get started.

Of course, it all depends on how motivated we are to move. Perhaps we need to leave Earth because a giant asteroid is coming to hit us. Or perhaps we ruin our climate to the point where Earth will become even more uninhabitable than Mars in the future. Given the right incentive, building giant solar mirror arrays and huge oxygen factories might be our best option. And look at it this way: the surface area of Mars is about 56 million square miles (or 1,559,000,000,000,000 square feet). So if we end up spending trillions of dollars to make Mars habitable, it would still be cheaper than buying real estate in California.

Can We Build a Warp Drive?

T he universe is achingly vast, and filled with fascinating places we'd love to explore. Unfortunately, it all seems to be out of our reach.

As we learned in a previous chapter, even if we could get a spaceship up to some reasonable fraction of the speed of light, it would take hundreds of thousands of years just to get to the other side of our galaxy, not to mention visit other galaxies (millions of years away) or even to push beyond the observable universe (hundreds of billions of years away).

And that is a definite limit. Few rules in the laws of physics are as hard and unbendable as the fact that nothing can move through space faster than the speed of light. This limit is based on our understanding of Einstein's theory of special relativity, which has been tested and probed and verified out the wazoo (and into the wazoo; really, we've tried *everything*).

It seems that the only way we'll reach the far edges of the universe is if we become a spacefaring civilization, hopping slowly from planet to planet over countless generations for millions or billions of years.

And yet it doesn't seem like that should be the case. We are conditioned by movies and books to think that the universe should be within our reach. That with the right technology, you can build vast space empires or explore other galaxies. You just hop on your spaceship, hit a button, and *whoosh*: the stars streak in front of you and light and energy swirl around you as you slip into "hyperspace," and then *boom*, you arrive millions of light-years away.

All you need is . . . a warp drive.

But what *is* a "warp drive"? Is it something that's totally in the world of fiction, or is it something that real physicists have considered? Is it possible to break the speed limit of the universe, the one that scientists cherish so much? Let's hit the button and see if we can warp our way to an answer.

Making Fiction Real

A lot of technological advances seem to happen in the following way:

Step #1: Science fiction author invents a new gadget, hand-waves the science.

Step #2: Physicists figure out how to make the gadget theoretically plausible, hand-wave how to build it.

Step #3: Engineers figure out how to build it, hand-wave how much it would cost.

Step #4: Yadda, yadda, yadda, it's now in your smartphone.

For warp drives, science fiction authors have done a solid job on Step #1, imagining portable warp drives that can take you to the stars. Now it's time for physicists to do their bit.

At first glance, you might think that physicists would say no. After all, a warp drive seems to break the one rule they seem pretty adamant about: getting somewhere faster than the speed of light. On this, physics will not wiggle or budge. *But*, if there's one thing most teenagers have learned, it's that if at first you don't get the answer you like, try asking a different question!

For example, if you ask the question, "Can we build spaceships that can travel through space faster than the speed of light?" the answer is a hard no. But if instead you ask the question, "Can we build spaceships that can get to places faster than light could have traveled there?" then you might notice physicists squirming a little before finally admitting, "Maybe." And every teenager knows that "maybe" is code for "I want to say no, but I need to check with your other parent."

The key difference in the two questions is the phrase "travel through space." If you read the fine print of special relativity, you learn that the speed limit applies to things moving *through* space. Now, that doesn't seem like it offers much of an opening, because doesn't everything move through space? The answer is yes, but the loophole is that space is . . . malleable.

"Conditions may vary. The Universe is not responsible for any damages due to irresponsible use of space..."

Who needs a lawyer when you have a physicist!

There are three general ways in which we can see a warp drive being feasible from a physics point of view:

◆ A hyperspace warp drive

◆ A wormhole-powered warp drive

◆ A space-bending warp drive

Let's get into each of these ideas and whether they are theoretically sound or even likely.

A Hyperspace (or Subspace, or Superspace) Warp Drive

In a lot of science fiction, the loophole for making a warp drive work is to leave our normal space (where the speed limit of the universe applies) and enter some other kind of space. Presumably, you can either go faster than light in this space or this space somehow connects the place where you are to the place where you are trying to go. Once you've traveled for some time in this hyperspace, you just slide back into normal space.

This approach works in fiction, allowing the characters and the story to span a whole galaxy without spending thousands of years sitting in a spaceship. But does this have a basis in real physics? Is there another kind of space that is parallel to our universe that we can somehow go into and out of?

One common idea that sometimes gets attached to this concept is the idea of "extra dimensions." We know that our space has three separate directions of possible motion: you can call them x, y, and z, but those are just arbitrary names. Some physicists suspect that there could be more ways that you could move, extra dimensions of space. It's hard to think about how that would work or where they would be, but it comes up often in string theory and other creative theories about gravity. According to such theories, these extra dimensions are not like ours: they curl around themselves and have different rules for how particles move through them.

That seems a lot like what we are looking for, right? Different parts of space with new sets of rules. Unfortunately, it's not as helpful as it might sound. These additional dimensions, if they exist, are not a different kind of space that's parallel to our space. They are just an extension of the space we have. They don't let you leave the space that you're in right now; they just give you more ways for your particles to wiggle or shimmy. It's like adding another line to your mailing address. It more accurately says where you are, but it doesn't provide your mail delivery person any shortcuts to bring you your mail faster.

There is one real physics theory that closely matches this idea of hyperspace: the multiverse. This is the idea that there could be other universes out there, either alternate versions of ours (split during quantum events) or other pockets of space with different laws of physics or different initial conditions.

If there are other universes, could they let us skip around our universe? Only if they were smaller or had higher top speeds than ours, and somehow connected to our universe in several different places. In that way, you could potentially jump into that universe, travel a short distance, and then connect back to our universe at a point that is really far away from where you started. And hey, maybe that other universe does look like a swirling tunnel of light and energy.

Sadly, though, the idea of the multiverse is still extremely theoretical. We don't have any reason to think it actually exists, other than to explain some weird quirks about our universe. And even if other universes do exist, physicists think the very thing that makes them appealing—their distinct rules of physics or alternate quantum variations—might also make it impossible for our universe to interact with them. So the most likely scenario is that we can never connect or travel between the different universes.

Wormhole Warp Drives

There are bizarre corners of our universe where space is bent and twisted beyond recognition, like no place we have ever known. The most famous members of this mysterious category are black holes, which are definitely not on the list of places we recommend you visit, since they are hard to survive and impossible to return from.

But there is a strange theoretical space-fold that might let you travel faster than light to a distant star: wormholes.

Wormholes are everywhere in science fiction. Writers use them as a shortcut between distant locations, to open portals to neighboring galaxies, to build exotic houses where every room is on a different planet, or to link planets into a galactic empire. In this way, you might imagine a wormhole as the basis of a warp drive: when you hit the button, you are opening and going through a wormhole that connects you to somewhere else in space.

At first glance, wormholes seem totally impossible. Wouldn't it count as faster-than-light travel, which is a big no-no according to physics? It's certainly true that travel from point A to point B is limited by the speed of light . . . but only if you go through all of the space between them.

While physics can't bend the rules, it turns out that the rules themselves allow for some bending of space and some strange connections. When you think of space, you probably imagine it as a flat backdrop for the action of the universe. But space is much more interesting than that, and it can have all sorts of interesting shapes and be connected in all sorts of ways. Space is actually part of the action, not just the backdrop, because it responds to the matter and energy inside of it. Matter and energy tell space how to bend, and space tells matter how to move. It's like a cosmic tango.

If it's totally empty, space is boring and simple. But if you plop a big fat star in the middle of it, the star will bend the space. That means that it changes the shape of space, and gets matter to find new, curved paths along it. That's why photons bend around massive objects even though they have no mass. They are just following the curvature of bent space. Physics tells us that space might be able to have any smoothly varying shape. And one of those shapes is a wormhole, a strange deformation of space that links two points that are far away from each other.

Wormholes actually have a close relationship with black holes. One way to make a wormhole is to connect two black holes by their singularities, which are the points of infinite density at the heart of each black hole. If the two black holes are far apart, then the wormhole is like a shortcut through space, creating a connection between the two points.

But this kind of wormhole doesn't help us at all. Why? Because even if you survived going into the first black hole (a tricky proposition in itself, as we've discussed) and traveled to the other side of the wormhole, you'd still be trapped inside the other black hole! You might have traveled to another part of space faster than light, but you are never leaving that point ever again.

The kind of wormhole that would be helpful for a warp drive is one that lets you escape out the other side. The only way to do that is to make a wormhole that connects a black hole to a "white hole." As we mentioned in an earlier chapter, white holes are theoretical objects, predicted by general relativity, that are the opposite of black holes. In a white hole, things can escape, but never enter. Think of the white hole as the exit point of the wormhole.

There are, obviously, a couple of problems with using this kind of wormhole for a warp drive.

First, it's a one-way connection. You might be able to fall into the black hole, pass through the wormhole, and then come out the white hole, but you can't go the other way. If you've figured out how to build wormholes and move their ends around, that might not be a problem for you, since you can just make another one to go back.

Second, it might be hard to survive the whole experience. Going into a black hole is no easy matter. Even if you pick a large black hole to go into to avoid getting ripped to shreds by its gravitational tidal forces, you still have to survive the trip to the middle of the black hole. And how do you squeeze yourself through a singularity?

For this, physics does have a cool answer: pick a spinning black hole. We prefer this kind of black hole because the center of it is not a tiny point but a spinning ring. Why is that? Things that fall into the black hole were probably spinning around it first, in the accretion disk. When they enter, that angular momentum can't just disappear. And since a point singularity has no size, it can't rotate and so it can't have any angular momentum. That's why a black hole with angular momentum has a ring at the center! And if it's connected to a white hole, then in principle you could pass through that ring and into the white hole.

A wormhole is also hard to keep open. The theory predicts that wormholes are prone to collapsing. The singularity ring at the center tends to pinch off and form two separate black holes with two

singularities. You definitely don't want to be in the middle when that happens.

The final problem with using a wormhole for a warp drive is that, so far, it's all very theoretical. Nobody has ever seen evidence that they actually exist. All of these fun ideas depend on general relativity being correct (and, so far, it has passed every experimental test). But we don't know whether it's right about super-extreme scenarios, like the center of black holes, where quantum physics can't be ignored.

We know black holes exist (we've seen those), but wormholes and white holes are still just an idea at this point. We don't even know how to make them. Nobody has yet found the recipe to make a wormhole, much less how to specify which points in space it connects. Think about it: your spaceship would need to have the ability to create a specific kind of black hole, and then somehow connect it to a white hole a long distance away.

Still, if you were to find a wormhole, or figure out how to get the

universe to make one on command, they could potentially be used to warp-speed your way to the other side of the universe.

Space-Bending Warp Drives

So if hyperspace doesn't really exist, and wormholes end up being too dangerous to go into, are there any other clever physics loopholes we can use to make a warp drive? As it turns out, the answer is yes.

Space is much more interesting than we first imagined. It isn't "nothing," but rather a thing that can wiggle (as gravitational waves), bend (which is what gravity is), and expand (as we've seen with dark energy and the expansion of the universe). It seems that space can be stretched or compressed in response to the mass and energy around it.

So what if instead of traveling *through* 4.2 light-years of space like a galactic newbie, we squeezed the space between here and the point where we want to go? And what if, at the same time, we expanded the space behind us?

The idea is to reduce the amount of space that you have to travel through. You could squeeze the space in front of you, cross it, and then expand the space behind you so that it goes back to normal. For example, each step would go something like this: you squeeze the 1,000 kilometers of space in front of you down to a tenth of a nanometer; then you move that tenth of a nanometer; and then you expand the space behind you back to its original 1,000 kilometers. The end result is that you only moved 0.1 nanometers, but you actually traversed 1,000 kilometers. If you can do this continually, your spaceship would sit in a kind of inverted warp bubble, moving you forward at an incredible rate. For you inside the inverted bubble, 4.2 light-years would become 4.2 *kilometers* that you have to cross. Then when you get there, you pop the ship out of the bubble, and presto, you have arrived!

It's a little like taking a moving walkway rather than actually walking. Physics is very strict about how quickly you can move along the walkway, but there's no speed limit to how fast the walkway itself can move. In the same way, physics has no limit to how quickly space can stretch or compress or move relative to itself.

But how do you *shrink* or *expand* space? What does that even mean?

Making space shrink or bend is not actually terribly tricky. You are doing it right now. And every time you visit the dessert bar and gain weight, you get better at it. Everything that has mass changes the shape of space. It's why Earth orbits the Sun: because the Sun's enormous mass has bent the shape of space like a bowling ball on a trampoline. The bending is intrinsic, changing the relative distance between bits of space-time.

Unfortunately, while physicists know that a warp bubble satisfies the equations of general relativity, they don't know how to arrange matter and energy to make one. It's like having the idea for a complicated dessert but no clue what the recipe is for baking it.

The trickiest part is that the back half of the warp bubble has to *expand* space. We know that mass and energy can compress space, but how do you expand it? All of the space in the universe is currently expanding, as it did quickly in the first few moments after the Big Bang, and that expansion is speeding up. We say that it's due to dark energy, but that doesn't mean we know what dark energy is. It's actually the other way around: "dark energy" is simply the term we use to describe the increasing expansion of the universe. We don't actually know what is causing it.

To expand space artificially, physicists have proposed another crazy idea: If you can shrink space with positive mass, can you expand space using *negative mass*?

Negative mass? What does that mean? As far as you know, everything around you has either zero mass (photons) or positive mass (you, matter, bananas). That's why we say that gravity is a purely attractive force. Unlike magnetism, which can attract (fridge magnets) or repel (maglev trains), gravity only seems to attract—because we've only seen positive mass.

Is negative mass possible? It's theoretically possible, but to date nobody has ever seen any matter with negative mass. It would be really weird stuff that acts in funny ways. Positive mass attracts, so if we put a blob of it next to a blob of negative mass, the negative mass would push away the positive mass, but the positive mass would pull on the negative mass. Like a teen soap opera where you never know who's chasing who, it gets confusing quickly.

Now, supposing that we figure out a way to make negative mass, could we then actually make a warp drive like this work? Sadly again, there are other limitations. Expanding and contracting space isn't something that comes cheap. It requires energy.

Physicists first estimated that the amount of matter or energy needed to bend the space in front of a warp drive was larger than all of the stuff in the universe. That's clearly not going to work. A bit of tweaking on the calculations brought the estimate down to requiring the energy equivalent of the entire mass of the planet Jupiter. A gas tank that big would probably make your spaceship really hard to parallel park when you arrive at that other galaxy.

There's been some talk of reducing this further, to reasonable levels, such as the energy equivalent of a one-ton mass. But so far, this is still in the "physicists discussing this in the break room" level of scientific research. No one has actually built or tested a space-compressing machine yet, so this is still pretty far off in the future.

Speaking of negative mass...

WARP DRIVE SYMPOSIUM

A Warped Answer

As much as we'd love to find a loophole to the speed limit of the universe and conquer the stars, it seems that the idea of a warp drive is still very much in the realm of fictional galactic space operas. But as always, it's good to remember that the universe is unpredictable, and that human progress and ingenuity are still on the rise. Maybe one day we will figure out the details for creating black and white holes and connecting them across space. Or maybe one day we will discover negative mass and new ways to harness energy to make devices that let us squeeze into a warp bubble and zip our way to other galaxies.

True, that's a lot of maybes. But if you ask your other parent, they might just let you get away with it.

When Will the Sun Burn Out?

Our sunny days are numbered.

From a distant ninety-three million miles away, the Sun seems to us like a strong, steady presence. It rises every day, without fail, and showers us with a constant stream of life-giving energy rays. But physicists have a very different view of the Sun.

Uh-oh.

To a physicist, the Sun is a constantly exploding nuclear bomb. This turbulent process releases vast amounts of energy, kept in check only by the sheer force of the Sun's gravity. The next time you enjoy a sunny afternoon, remember that you are toasting your toes to the light of a nuclear explosion. But physicists also know that underneath this incredibly tumultuous phenomenon there are mechanisms conspiring to end it, and that there's an internal clock steadily ticking down to zero. The physics of the Sun reveal that its days of shining brightly will someday end.

Take cover!

Is this going to happen anytime soon, or do we have billions of years to plan for it? Let's find out exactly how many sunny days we have left.

A Star's Birth
(5 billion years ago; Sun's age: 0)

To understand why and when the Sun will eventually die, we first have to go back to its beginnings.

The Sun wasn't born in some fiery, dramatic event. There wasn't even a little bang. Instead, there was a gradual accumulation of gas and dust. Most of the gas was plain old hydrogen, which has been the most common element in the universe since there *was* a universe. But there were other, heavier elements, too: leftover bits from nearby stars that had already lived and died by the time our Sun came around.

These vast, swirling clouds were slowly gathered together by gravity, which is the weakest (yet most persistent) force in the universe. But the gas and dust particles in these hot and swirling clouds were moving too fast to be completely held together by gravity, and they resisted forming dense clumps.

Scientists aren't sure what eventually triggered the formation of

TOO HOT TO CLUMP

our Sun. It could be that magnetic fields helped trap the particles and channeled them close together. Or it could be that some external event, like a shock wave from a nearby supernova, pushed the gas particles together tightly. Or maybe it was just time: eventually the gas cloud cooled, and the slower-moving particles started to fall toward the center.

Whatever the cause, enough stuff eventually clumped together to start a runaway process. Gas and dust gathered in one place, which led to stronger gravity, which attracted more gas and dust, which led to more gravity, and so on. Eventually, enough gas and dust had gathered in one place to form the beginnings of a star. And that's when things really started to heat up.

A STAR IS BORN

Fusion Pushes Back

(4.9 billion years ago; Sun's age: 0.1 billion years old)

After about one hundred thousand years, gravity had done its job of pulling together a huge cloud of mostly hydrogen. At first, the individual molecules resisted. They don't enjoy being crowded that close together because the positive charges of their protons repel each other. Getting two protons close together is like trying to put a cat into a bucket of water: you have to really want it. Fortunately, gravity never gives up. Over time, the enormous accumulated mass kept pushing and pushing the protons together until something finally snapped.

If protons come close enough together, they overcome their repulsion and start to *attract* each other. That's because a different force starts to act: the strong nuclear force. This may be the one thing in particle physics that is well named, because the strong force is, well, *strong*. Over long distances, it's not very powerful, but at short distances, it's much stronger than the electrical repulsion that keeps protons apart. Once this strong force brings the protons together, something incredible happens: fusion.

Electromagnetic
Repulsion

Strong Force
Attraction

The nuclei of the two hydrogen atoms stick together and, after a few more steps, eventually form a new element, helium. People tried for centuries to convert one kind of element into another (usually lead into gold) and failed for so long that the entire endeavor, known as "alchemy," was written off as crackpottery. It turns out that it's totally possible, but only under special conditions, like being at the center of the Sun.*

The amazing thing about fusing hydrogen into helium is that it releases a lot of energy. The helium that is made actually has less mass than the original hydrogen atoms, and the extra mass gets converted into energy, which is then carried off by neutrinos and photons. If you're confused by how making a bond can release energy, just think of the opposite case: it usually *takes* energy to *break* a bond.

This simple mechanism is what lights up the entire universe. Because fusion is happening inside of countless stars, we don't have to live in a dark void. And gravity is what makes this possible, by pushing reluctant protons together until they fuse. But now comes the backlash.

The energy released by the fusion reactions rushes out, pushing everything outward and keeping gravity from further squeezing the protons together. Suddenly, we have two cosmic forces in an

---

* This fusion only happens if you have enough mass to generate the gravity needed to squeeze protons together. If you only have the mass of, say, Jupiter, then you just become a planet. If Jupiter had a hundred times more mass, fusion would start to happen at its core and it would become a red dwarf star.

epic tug-of-war: gravity fighting to squeeze everything together, and fusion releasing energy that pushes back on gravity. These two forces get locked into a solar stalemate that lasts billions of years.

The Long, Slow Burn

(4.9 billion years ago to 5 billion years in the future; Sun's age: 0.1 billion to 10 billion years old)

For the next ten billion years, the Sun is like an active war zone between two impressive forces: gravity and fusion. Gravity, the original actor in this drama, keeps squeezing and pushing together all the material in the star. But the energy being created by fusion pushes everything outward. The star burns and shines and lives on in this precarious balance for billions of years.

And this is where we are now. When you look up at the Sun (not directly, hopefully), you are watching a giant ball that is both exploding and collapsing at the same time. It's hard to grasp the scale of what's happening inside the Sun. Beyond the fusion core at the center, there are 350,000 miles of layers of hot, churning plasma. Photons being created by the core bounce around in these layers until, fifty thousand years later, their energy finally bursts free and out into space. Eight minutes later, some of them make their way here to give us sunshine.

The Sun has been burning this way for the last 4.9 billion years, and it will continue to do so for the next 5 billion years. The balance between gravity and fusion doesn't last forever, though. Silently, a clock has started counting down within the star.

Gravity is weak but relentless. It will continue to pull on all the material inside the star forever. But fusion requires fuel (hydrogen) and produces waste (helium), which limits how long it can keep going. At first, the helium collects at the center of the star, slowly accumulating there and not bothering anybody. But eventually, it will start to change the star.

Helium is denser than hydrogen, and so the core becomes heavier, increasing the gravitational squeeze on the hydrogen that's now mostly outside the core. As a result, there are more fusion reactions in the outer layers, which makes the Sun hotter, brighter, and larger. The reactions grow slowly—every one hundred million years, the Sun gets 1 percent brighter. But it adds up. In four billion years, the

Sun will be 40 percent brighter than it is today, causing our oceans to boil.

As fusion burns even hotter, the Sun grows larger and larger. Fusion appears to be winning, but it's consuming its fuel faster and faster, and like a rock star on a bender, it will eventually crash and burn.

Getting Bigger in Old Age

(5 billion to 6.4 billion years in the future; Sun's age: 10 billion to 11.4 billion years old)

The battle between gravity and fusion lasts for billions of years, with fusion appearing to get the upper hand. Ten billion years after it started, fusion becomes so powerful that it actually reverses some of gravity's gains, pushing the outer hydrogen layers of the Sun back out.

At that time, about five billion years from now, the Sun will grow to two hundred times its current size, nearly enveloping Earth and all of the inner planets. Most of the Sun will be the fluffy outer layers of hydrogen, which will be cooler relative to the rest of the Sun. But by Earth standards it will be unbearably hot, and life anywhere in the inner solar system will be essentially impossible.

This dramatic display of fusion's power is its last hurrah. Having knocked gravity back on its heels, fusion overextends itself and starts to falter. But before it finally succumbs to gravity, it has one more trick up its sleeve.

One Last Fling

(6.4 billion to 6.5 billion years in the future; Sun's age: 11.4 billion to 11.5 billion years old)

At 11.4 billion years old (6.4 billion years from now), the Sun will have burned all the hydrogen in its core, exhausting the fuel that powered its battle with gravity. While fusion can continue to burn in the layers of hydrogen surrounding the core, it can no longer push against gravity's pressure inside the core.

Fusion isn't done yet, though. When gravity has compressed the helium core so much that the atoms get squeezed together, fusion starts to do the same thing it did with hydrogen. In a flash, it begins joining helium atoms together into heavier elements, mainly carbon. This is a literal flash, not a metaphorical one. When it's sparked, helium fusion releases as much light as the *entire galaxy*. Fortunately, this takes place inside the Sun, so the light doesn't burn humanity's colonies on the moons of Jupiter.

The carbon that the fusion reaction makes is concentrated at the core, making our Sun a triple-decker sandwich of carbon, then helium, then hydrogen. In larger stars, the cycle goes on to produce heavier elements.* But our Sun isn't massive enough to fuse carbon, so eventually the helium and hydrogen are exhausted and the Sun simply . . . fizzles out.

This period of helium fusion starts with a bang, but it doesn't last very long. While the Sun burned hydrogen for ten billion years, it will only burn helium for about one hundred million years.

Jupiter Goes Bonkers

(6.5 billion years in the future; Sun's age: 11.5 billion years old)

With all of its fuel exhausted, fusion sputters out. The outer shells of the Sun will drift out and form a nebula, the raw materials for future planetary formation. As fusion fades, gravity continues to work on the core, gathering the remaining elements into a very hot, dense blob known as a "white dwarf." This smaller star is about half of the original Sun's mass, but compressed into a ball about the size of Earth.

And this drives the outer planets, which survived the Sun's expansion, to a dangerous state. Because the Sun loses half of its mass, it doesn't pull on Jupiter and the outer planets as much. This makes

---

* For massive stars, the pressure gets so great at the core that carbon fuses into oxygen, which can fuse into neon, and so on. Each step is more rapid, but in the largest stars, it continues until it makes iron. Iron can't be naturally fused, because it would absorb energy rather than release it, and so this is the end of the road for fusion.

THE SUN SIMMERS

the gas giants relax their orbit to about twice the previous distance from the Sun. That sounds like a good move, given the Sun's previously fiery antics, but it makes those planets much more susceptible to gravitational tugs from nearby stars that pass by. In many scenarios, the orbits of Jupiter and Saturn become much more chaotic, ejecting the other remaining planets (Neptune and Uranus) from the solar system until only they remain. Eventually, only one remains, likely Jupiter, a solo gas giant orbiting the dead core of our Sun.

There's no fusion happening at this point, but the white dwarf still shines. Like a white-hot piece of metal pulled out of a forge, it glows from its own internal heat, and it will do so for a long time.

And now the Sun is stuck. The temperature isn't high enough to start fusion, and gravity isn't powerful enough to squeeze the atoms closer and upgrade the star further into a neutron star or a black hole.

The End (Trillions of Years from Now)

How long does a white dwarf shine? We don't actually know because we've never seen one dim. Physicists think that it may take *trillions* of years to cool down, eventually becoming a dark, dense mass known as a "black dwarf." But the universe just isn't old enough for any black dwarfs to exist right now.

This means that our Sun may exist as a white dwarf for a long time, maybe even trillions of years. It won't be as hot or as bright as it was in its youth, but it might be warm enough to sustain human life, once we abandon our temporary colonies on Jupiter and settle in closer to it. Perhaps as we sit around the embers of that white dwarf, humanity will tell stories of what life was like in our day, when the Sun burned and humans took it for granted. We'll reminisce about how it was a continual explosion, and it seemed like the sunny days would last forever.

Why Do We Ask Questions?

Of course, we saved the best for last.

People have asked us a lot of very fascinating questions over the years. The range of topics varies a lot, from intricate and niche ("Why do photons get bent by gravity if they have no mass?") to profound ("Why does the universe exist at all?"). And in this book, we tried to give answers to the most frequently asked questions—the ones that tap into our shared curiosity about the universe and that seem to be most on top of people's minds.

But there is one frequently asked question that we haven't answered yet. In fact, it's probably the most frequently asked question we get. We saved it for last because we think it's the most important question we typically get about the universe. Are you ready? Here it is:

What does that even mean?

Okay, that's probably not the question you were expecting. It probably doesn't even feel like a complete question to you. Grammatically speaking, your high school English teacher would cringe. Still, it comes up a lot.

The interesting thing about "What does that even mean?" is that it's not the first question that people even *want* to ask us. Usually, we see this question added *after* their actual question. For example, people will sometimes write us and ask, "Hey, Daniel and Jorge, is the universe really fourteen billion years old? And what does that even mean?" Or, "Say, where does the energy to expand the universe come from? Can it really come from nothing? What does that even mean?"

In fact, we're guessing that "What does that even mean?" is not a question that most people were even *expecting* to ask. And yet there it usually is, added haphazardly to the end of whatever question they initially wanted us to answer.

At first glance, it may look like an afterthought or a random throwaway line. But actually, we think it's the most telling part of their question. That's because it reflects the true reason they were asking their question in the first place.

Here's what we think happens: People typically have an initial question that gets them curious. It might be about the age of the universe or about the nature of matter and energy in our cosmos. It could be something that they heard about in our podcast or read somewhere else. Whatever it was, it got the gears in their heads turning, and eventually it crystallized in the form of a specific question. But then as soon as the question left their mouth or their typing fingertips, a thought probably occurred to them: *What do I do with the answer if I get one?* And when they consider all the consequences that an answer might imply, a small voice inside of them whispers in their ear: *And what does that even mean?*

What does it mean that the universe is fourteen billion years old?

Or what does it mean that the universe is expanding out of nothing?

You see, it's not enough to know the answer to a question. The answer could be "yes" or "no" or "it comes from the Schwarzschild self-interaction of the vacuum Higgs fluctuations," but in the end the specifics don't matter. What ultimately matters is the *meaning* of the answers—the significance for how you live your life.

You might not think that the answer to the question "Where did the universe come from?" could change your life. But even if the answer doesn't affect the details of your life in a practical way, it can change something even more important: the *context* of your life. Fundamental answers can impact how you see yourself and how you relate to the wider universe. For example, learning that Earth is not the center of the cosmos made humanity realize that we are a small part of something larger, and that we are not on the universe's main stage. In the same way, discovering that the universe is filled with intelligent life—or that intelligence is extremely rare, or even that we are the only thinking beings in the universe—would deeply affect how we see ourselves and how unique we think we are.

It's that search for meaning and context that gives these questions their cosmic power. We want to not just *know* an answer; we want to understand it, because that understanding changes how we frame our existence. It can take us off the stage that we thought we were living on and reveal that we have been dancing on a completely different one.

The most tantalizing thing about the answers to scientific questions is that they are within our grasp. For each of the questions in this book, and for every science question you can imagine, there *is* an answer. It might be hidden, or far away, or at a scale too small for us to see right now, but the answers are *there*.

We may one day be able to answer all the questions in this book. But even then, we might have no choice but to append the same follow-up question that our listeners ask: *And what does that even mean?*

That's the one question we can't answer in this book. Why? Because the answer is different for each of us. We all get to define our own context and find our own significance in this universe. It's asking these questions that reveals who we are and why we search for meaning.

So what are *your* frequently asked questions?

Acknowledgments

Another frequently asked question we get is, "How do you find the time to write a book?" The answer is: with a little help from a lot of people!

We are grateful to friends and colleagues who reviewed early versions of the manuscript: Flip Tanedo, Kev Abazajian, Jasper Halekas, Robin Blume-Kahout, Nir Goldman, Leo Stein, Claus Kiefer, Aaron Barth, Paul Robertson, Steven White, Bob McNees, Steve Chesley, James Kasting, and Suelika Chial.

Special thanks to our editor, Courtney Young, for her continued faith and trust in us and her steady guidance; and to Seth Fishman for always finding the right place for our work. Thanks to the whole team at the Gernert Company, including Rebecca Gardner, Will Roberts, Ellen Goodson Coughtrey, Nora Gonzalez, and Jack Gernert, and to their international counterparts. Many thanks to everyone at Riverhead Books who contributed their time and talent to the making and release of this book, including Jacqueline Shost, Ashley Sutton, Kasey Feather, and May-Zhee Lim. We are also grateful to Georgina Laycock for planting the seed of the idea for this book (and the title!), and to the entire team at John Murray.

Jorge is grateful to his family, as always, for their continued support and encouragement.

Most of all, we are grateful to our readers, listeners, and fans, who have followed what we do over the years, and for their amazing questions.

Index

Page numbers in *italics* refer to illustrations.